E ISLAND
LLEJO

Suisun Bay

RQUINEZ STRAIT

PITTSBURG

ANTIOCH

San Joaquin River

MT. TAMALPAIS

Bridge

RED ROCK

CALIFORNIA PT.

RICHMOND

MILL VALLEY

PT. RICHMOND

RICHARDSON BAY

TIBURON

EL CERRITO

BELVEDERE

Raccoon Strait

BROOKS ISLAND

HOSPITAL COVE

ANGEL ISLAND

SAUSALITO

ALBANY

PT. KNOX

PT. BLUNT

San Francisco Bay

HORSESHOE BAY

LIME PT.

BERKELEY PIER

BERKELEY

PT. BONITA

PT. DIABLO

Golden Gate Bridge

ALCATRAZ ISLAND

Golden Gate

FORT POINT

BLOSSOM ROCK

TREASURE ISLAND

SAND ISLAND

MILE ROCK

LANDS END

PT. LOBOS

Presidio

Fisherman's Wharf

EMERYVILLE

SEAL ROCKS

Sea Cliff

Cliff House

YERBA BUENA ISLAND

Golden Gate Park

Bay Bridge

RINCON PT.

OAKLAND

Pacific Ocean

SAN FRANCISCO

ALAMEDA

HUNTERS POINT

HB

San Francisco Bay

J. L. Feighan

San Francisco Bay

Doubleday & Company, Inc., Garden City, New York

Harold Gilliam

1957

Library of Congress Catalog Card Number 57–10453
Copyright © 1957 by Harold Thompson Gilliam
All Rights Reserved
Printed in the United States of America
First Edition
Designed by Diana Klemin

For Ann

Acknowledgments

The writer expresses his great appreciation to the dozens of people whose kindness made this book possible (but who are not to be held responsible for any errors on the part of the author). Among them: the late Joseph Henry Jackson, for advice and encouragement at the project's inception; Jack Foisie, marine reporter of the San Francisco *Chronicle;* Robert T. Orr, curator of birds and mammals, California Academy of Sciences; the late Edward F. McCarthy, assistant manager, Marine Exchange; Howard C. Wood, principal bridge engineer, San Francisco-Oakland Bay Bridge; Clifford E. Paine, consulting engineer, and James Adam, general manager, Golden Gate Bridge and Highway District; George P. Hammond, director, Bancroft Library, University of California; Norman E. A. Hinds, professor of geology, University of California; R. Corday Counts, meteorologist in charge, U. S.

Weather Bureau, San Francisco Airport Station; Arnold Court, consultant in climatology, W. I. Follett, curator of ichthyology, and George W. Bunton, curator of astronomy, California Academy of Sciences; Glen Logan, supervising engineer, Twelfth Coast Guard District; Francis P. Filice, associate professor of biology, University of San Francisco; C. A. Kester, U. S. Coast and Geodetic Survey; Nino Geraldi, Fishermen's Grotto, Fisherman's Wharf; Stanleigh Arnold, Sunday editor, San Francisco *Chronicle;* John Reber; Donald D. Royer, Angel Island State Park supervisor; Lt. Tom Marlatt, U. S. Army; Thelma Weber, librarian, and her assistants, San Francisco *Chronicle.*

Thanks are due also to the San Francisco *Chronicle* for permission to reprint material which originally appeared in its pages; to the California Department of Water Resources; the Twelfth Coast Guard District; the San Francisco Bar Pilots; the Leslie Salt Co.; the California Historical Society; the California Academy of Sciences; and the Corps of Engineers, U. S. Army.

Finally, the author owes thanks—beyond all possibility of adequate acknowledgment here—to Mary Lou Mueller, whose editorial skill, patience, and wisdom throughout the preparation of the manuscript have been in large measure responsible for whatever merit this book possesses.

For further reading on the subject of the bay's ferries the reader is referred to *Of Walking Beams and Paddle Wheels,* by George H. Harlan and Clement Fisher, Jr., and *Recollections of a Tule Sailor,* by John Leale, and for historical background to *The Western Gate, a San Francisco Reader,* edited by Joseph Henry Jackson.

Contents

5

Flood and Flow 67

6

"Harbor of Harbors" 90

9

Shipwrecks 185

10

The Changing Shoreline 207

11

Islands of Time 226

12

Tides in the Sky 267

13

The Bridges 293

14

Tide of Empire 324

1

The Western Gate

This is the place where the Pacific, eternally assaulting the land, has breached the thousand-mile mountain barrier at the western edge of the continent.

Its rhythmic tides surge between the dark red cliffs on either side of the strait, flood the long basin in the coastal hills, and cleave through the inner rim of mountains into the heart of the Central Valley.

Out of this violent meeting of land and sea was born the bay named for St. Francis of Assisi.

Long rolling combers from off the deeps of the ocean explode into geysers of spray in its headlands. Giant winds roar through its entrance, bringing the life-giving moisture of the sea to the arid inner valleys, creating the great summer fogs which pour through the strait in massive flowing forms like the advance of a living glacier.

This is the incomparable harbor that remained hidden behind the mountain wall for more than two centuries while scores of navigators sailed along the coast without sighting its entrance.

This is the bay that was the focal point of the greatest treasure hunt in history when the modern Argonauts sailed their thousand ships here and set out for gold.

And this is the mountain-bordered inland sea which became the nerve center of a western empire, rimmed by a dozen cities, harboring ships and planes from around the world. Yet its waves still wash remote shores where deer and beaver and mink come to the water's edge, where sea lions roar, where great flocks of sea birds stop off in their long migrations down the flyways of the hemisphere.

This bay is two trillion gallons of salt water covering four hundred square miles. It is one of the great ports of the earth, contains the nation's largest naval base, and subsumes a number of subsidiary bays, including Richardson, San Pablo, and Suisun. It is the only outlet to the sea for the sixty-thousand-square-mile Central Valley of California; into it flow the waters of sixteen rivers.

It encloses ten islands and is spanned by the world's greatest bridges. Its opaque surface hides swarming colonies of marine life from shrimps to sharks, and its channels carry currents mightier than the continent's biggest rivers.

It is a mirror of the sky, reflecting the sparkle of noonday sun, the gray of summer fogs, the alabaster white of floating clouds, the crimson and purple of twilight, the jeweled amber lamps of its long arching bridges, the shimmer of moonrise above the eastern mountains.

It tempers the weather; affects the winds, fogs, and rains that move across its surface; influences the crops and industries around it; and shapes in countless ways the lives of the three million people who live and work on its shores. . . .

Floyd Dickerson, driving down the winding levees between the salt ponds which border the southern end of the bay for thirty miles, stops his car and looks out across the briny acres, where a stiff norther is scudding salt foam into drifts. He gets out, walks slowly for a quarter of a mile, checking the levees closely.

The wind is cold, and he turns his face occasionally to avoid the icy salt spray. Finding no damage to the levees from the wind-driven water, he returns to the car, shivering slightly, hoping that whatever housewife seasons her cooking with the salt from this pond a year or so from now will appreciate his trouble. . . .

A hundred yards out of Sausalito yacht harbor, businessman Dick Simon switches off the auxiliary engine of his thirty-six-foot ketch, the *Kia-Ora,* and gives the word to his volunteer crew to hoist the sails. As the wind hits the canvas, suddenly, like a deer rousing from sleep, the yacht is alert and tense, responding tautly to every influence—the breeze, the currents, the tightening of the sails, the hand at the tiller. Salt spray flies from her bow as she leans to the leeward. Simon turns up his collar, grinning happily. . . .

In the little white Marine Exchange lookout station on the end of Meiggs Wharf, protruding into the bay next to San Francisco's Aquatic Park, chief lookout Ed McCarthy spots the bow of a ship coming into view under the Golden Gate Bridge.

Although he recognizes the ship from long experience, as a matter of routine he swings his long telescope around on its tripod, checks the name on the bow, and notes her signal flags. She is the liner *President Cleveland*, thirteen days out of Yokohama via Honolulu. She flies the red and white signal flag signifying that a pilot is on board and the yellow pennant signaling a request for a routine inspection by U. S. Public Health authorities.

McCarthy checks his watch and lifts the phone connecting him directly with Marine Exchange headquarters in the Ferry Building.

"Steamer *President Cleveland* coming in under the bridge at 11:37 . . ."

The alert goes out from the Ferry Building to American President Lines offices on California Street, to the Red Stack tug dispatcher at Pier 25, to the Bar Pilots on Pier 7, to shipyards, patrol services, Navy headquarters, government offices, and a dozen other agencies around the bay: "*President Cleveland*, under the bridge at 11:37 . . ."

At precisely 5:17 P.M. Ed Schneider, the keeper of the Alcatraz light, begins his climb up the 128 steps of the island's tower. At the top he pauses for breath, pulls up the shades that protect the lens from the sun, carefully wipes the windows, then the lens itself.

He looks briefly out across the island, sees no one but a few children playing around the guards' quarters. He reflects that it has been a quiet job, these twenty-six years—except for the time the Marines landed and gunfire crackled across the island for two days.

Schneider opens the switch box, flips on the light and the motor which turns it, and walks again down the long spiral stairs. On the bridge of a ship crossing the bar, ten miles out, the pilot catches the light's quick gleam directly over his vessel's bow. . . .

Secretary Eleanor Linton climbs the stairs to her Telegraph Hill apartment at the end of the day, her head still throbbing with images of business letters, filing cabinets, shorthand notes, and typewriter keys. Inside she sinks in a chair by a window overlooking the Embarcadero.

Directly below, the big white *Lurline* is being nudged out of the dock by tugs, her decks crowded with Hawaii-bound passengers. A long gray aircraft carrier passes Alcatraz, the crew standing in formation on the flight deck. A yellow helicopter hovers just above the pier where the old windjammer *Balclutha* spreads her spars against the bay. The late afternoon sun is touching the water with gold, and from the Gate comes a cool salt breeze.

The secretary pushes the window open wide and breathes deeply. . . .

In his one-cylinder fishing boat off China Camp on the Marin shore, Pete Ghio hauls up his net from the bottom of the bay and dumps the squirming mass onto the deck—small flopping bullheads, big blobs of jellyfish, several large crabs that scuttle across the deck, and a three-foot leopard shark that he quickly grabs by the tail and tosses back in the water. Shrimps, the real pay catch, are disappointingly scarce—hardly enough to make a shrimp salad for somebody's lunch at Fisherman's Wharf tomorrow.

The fisherman looks up; the wind is blowing from the southeast, and the sky is streaked with high feathery cirrus clouds, signs of an approaching storm. Good. If the rivers rise and flow brown and muddy into the bay, flushing out the shrimp, tomorrow will be better. . . .

THE CITY

It has been said that all great cities of history have been built on bodies of water—Rome on the Tiber, Paris on the Seine, London on the Thames, New York on the Hudson. If this is a criterion of a city's greatness, surely San Francisco ranks in the first magnitude among cities of the world. For never was a metropolis more dominated by any natural feature than San Francisco by its bay.

In Rome, Paris, London, New York, once away from the water's edge you quickly lose track of it in the buzzing swarm of the city's interior. But San Francisco lies at the tip of a peninsula, and anywhere within the city's forty-five square miles a view of the water is only a few steps away at most— to the head of the block or the roof of the building or the top of the hill.

East of the peninsula's central ridges the city slants toward the bay. All of the downtown district and the older residential areas lie within the valleys and hills of this eastward slope. The salt fragrance of the wind penetrates every neighborhood. The bass drones of the foghorns and the whistles of ships are as common as the sound of automobile horns in the streets.

You can climb Twin Peaks and see several hundred square miles of bay spread around you like a glowing tapestry of light and color. More often the bay's impact comes unexpectedly. Rounding a corner in the heart of the city, you come upon it suddenly in the distance between nearby houses, blue in the sun. Waiting for an elevator in a downtown building, you glance out the window and are startled to see a high swinging arc of the Bay Bridge and the white ferry passing the base of one of its towers.

The bay seems always around you. It shines in the distance beyond the long rows of bulging bay-windowed flats. It appears at the bottom of the streets that drop dizzily down from the city's heights. It glows beyond the narrow, cluttered alleys of Chinatown.

It hits you with a quick blow in the innards as you drive over a rise of Russian Hill and see its sudden gleam and sparkle between nearby trees. It comes to you as a series of brief, breath-catching vignettes as you rise on the Powell cable car over Nob Hill and get successive glimpses of it at the ends of the cross streets—a shining shield of blue spanned by the giant bridge arching across the water to the cities and hills of the far shore.

2

In the Beginning

The Indians believed that the bay was created suddenly: One morning the earth rumbled and shook; the mountains split asunder, forming the Golden Gate; and the ocean charged through in a wave, producing the bay by a single, cataclysmic inundation.

The legend has a melodramatic appeal, but the truth—or as much of it as geologists have been able to piece together—is far more impressive.

Nature's masterpieces are not created in a day. The bay is the child of the elements, working ponderously through aeons of time. It was conceived out of a series of titanic conflicts between the ocean and the continent. It was born slowly, out of the travail of earth. . . .

The Rise of the Coast Range   Go to Land's End at the

outer rim of the Golden Gate, where the surf batters the continent's edge, and gaze westward into the past.

There, if the day is clear, you can see on the ocean horizon two dark specks of land, only their peaks visible above the curve of the earth. You are looking nearly a hundred million years back into time.

These are the Farallon Islands, barren rock relics of a long land mass that once stretched for two hundred miles north and south, predecessor of this peninsula on which you stand, of the present bay, and of the land around its shores.

A million centuries ago, when the great dinosaurs roamed the earth, this area was part of a vast inland sea, an arm of the Pacific. From the peaks of the Farallon land mass to the Sierra Nevada two hundred miles to the east, all of California lay beneath the ocean waiting to be born.

Now look northwest along the Marin coast past Bolinas Head to the long arm of land jutting into the ocean on the horizon. This is the Point Reyes peninsula, once part of that same Farallon land mass and now geologically related to the islands rather than to the mainland.

Even today the relationship is visible. Drive out the Point Reyes road past Tomales Bay, climb the western ridge of the peninsula and suddenly you are in another world. The aspect of the land drastically changes. From lush canyons of Douglas fir and redwood you suddenly emerge on a windswept mesa bending toward the ocean, often enshrouded in heavy mists. Certain kinds of vegetation, such as the flat-topped bishop pines, grow only on this ancient tableland and similar isolated areas.

Down the center of the long narrow valley which joins this peninsula to the mainland (and which is now partly filled by Tomales and Bolinas bays) runs the San Andreas fault. It was along this ancient rift that the earth shuddered convulsively early one April morning in 1906 and destroyed most of San Francisco.

Back in the Cretaceous period when this story begins, one hundred million years ago, the land mass west of the fault extended southward from Point Reyes to the Farallones and on to what is now the Salinas Valley—and because of its relation to the latter area is known to geologists as Salinia.

Salinia was not then, however, as bleak as Point Reyes and the Farallones are today. Climate, like the face of the land, undergoes drastic changes throughout geologic time. Torrential rains once pelted down on the mountains of Salinia, drummed on the broad leaves of tropical trees and plants, sank into the soft, spongy soil, or ran off and collected in rivers which gouged the land and flowed in torrents into the ocean.

Powerful currents carried the muddy waters far offshore to the east. There the silt and sand sank slowly to the bottom, grain after grain, layer after layer, for years and centuries and millenniums. The increasing weight bore heavily down on the ocean floor until the crust of the earth itself sagged beneath the burden of sedimentary layers six miles deep.

Eventually the strain became too great. Pressured from above by the unbearable weight of the accumulated sediments, from below by the hot mass of the earth's interior, the rock of the ocean floor slowly crumpled and gave way. Molten masses flowed hot from below and gradually cooled beneath the sea.

Slowly the folds of the buckled ocean floor began to appear above the surface, washed over at first by waves and high tides, then forming into a long, low land mass—predecessor of the present Coast Range.

For millions of years the land rose and fell like slow ocean waves. California, lying at the edge of the continent, was one of the earth's most turbulent areas. Both Salinia and the newly born Coast Range sank beneath the sea and rose again; only the far Sierra Nevada remained continually above water. But at some period during the last million years, the Coast Range began to take the shape it was to have when man arrived on the scene.

Gradually the inland sea between the Coast Range and the Sierra dried out and became the Central Valley. Salinia eroded away until there was nothing left but residues like the granite rocks of the Farallones and the barren mesa of the Point Reyes peninsula. The land forms of California had achieved their present basic contours, and the stage was set for the second act of the drama.

The Carving of the Gate   Throughout the Pleistocene epoch, beginning a million years ago, invisible moisture, rising from the ocean in eternal cycles of evaporation, gathered into clouds and was carried east by prevailing ocean winds over the newborn Coast Range and across the valley to the massive wall of the Sierra Nevada.

There the clouds piled up against the mountain barrier, spilling their burden of moisture, falling as rain on the foothills and as snow among the high granite peaks. Steadily, as the snow melted and the underground reservoirs flowed out in springs, the waters poured in cascades and rapids down the mountains to the Central Valley and formed rivers which made their way through gaps in the Coast Range back to their source in the ocean. The cycle was completed.

But the Coast Range continued to rise, and there began a long struggle between two mighty forces—the rivers, flowing westward to the sea, and the mountains, rising to block their courses. Beneath the mountains was the accumulated pressure of the compressing rock of the earth's crust. Behind the rivers was the force of all the falling waters of the Sierra—ten thousand springs, rivulets, creeks, and streams drawn irresistibly toward the sea.

One by one the rivers were blocked by the rising Coast Range until a single outlet was left to the ocean. Here the waters of the four-hundred-mile-long valley and its surrounding mountains converged into one great torrent to pour through the last remaining pass.

As the mountains continued to rise, the river picked up the particles of earth in its path and carried them downstream, using them as tools to scour out its channel to the sea. Ultimately the grinding force of the swiftly flowing river won the contest. The stream sliced its way westward through the rising mountains, cut a deep gorge through the first series of ridges, flowed southward several miles through a rolling valley, and turned west again to carve another gorge through a final barrier to the sea.

The first gorge is now the strait of Carquinez. The other is the Golden Gate. The valley between became part of the basin of the present bay.

Stand now on a shore of the Golden Gate and look at the geologic record of this gargantuan conflict between river and mountains. On either side of the strait are the dark red cliffs of Franciscan sandstone where the river carved its way through the rising hills and exposed layer after layer of the underlying strata, now twisted and upended, originally washed from the slopes of Salinia and deposited here when this area was sea bottom. Up at Carquinez, twenty-five miles northeast, you can read the same story in the cliffs, where the river cut another channel through the rising Berkeley Hills.

Three hundred thousand years ago this bay was a river valley broken by the ridges which would someday be known by such names as Potrero San Pablo, Tiburon, San Mateo Point, and Coyote Hills. High on the valley's western rim stood the long-ridged peak of Tamalpais. Rising from the valley floor were high points which would one day be islands—Yerba Buena, Angel, Belvedere, Alcatraz. A small stream drained the shallow canyon now occupied by San Francisco's Market Street and followed the north side of a curving ridge which would eventually support the world's longest suspension bridge.

Having carved Carquinez Strait and the Golden Gate, the river continued to transport great quantities of silt, sand, and gravel down its course through the valley, carrying most of the load out beyond the Golden Gate to drop it on the ocean floor. Slowly a marshy delta rose above the low-tide level outside the Gate until after millenniums it extended more than thirty miles out to sea. Probably if there had been humans inhabiting the valley in those days, it would have been possible for them to walk to the Farallones at low tide.

The Big Thaw   These events took place during the Pleistocene, epoch of the great glaciers. Icy winds whipped down the valley in the wintertime and snow fell thickly on the surrounding mountains. Far to the east, the Sierra Nevada—like most of the northern part of the continent—was covered with masses of ice; glaciers thousands of feet deep were at work along the entire axis of the range, remodeling in that massive block of granite the great Sierra canyons like Yosemite, Kings, and Tuolumne.

Then, some 225,000 years ago, from some cause as unaccountable as that which had brought the ice in the first place, the weather slowly began to grow warmer. Winter snows fell lighter and melted earlier. The sun's rays beat down on the Sierra glaciers, and melting ice ran into rivulets.

Dry mountain gullies became creeks. Creeks swelled into rivers. The great river system draining the center of California cut deeper in its channels and flooded its banks, carrying ever-increasing amounts of soil down to the delta outside the Golden Gate.

But the delta, instead of growing larger as the river added greater amounts of material, began to shrink. What the river added, the ocean took away. Around the world, the icecap was melting, and the water from all the swollen rivers of North America, Europe, and Asia poured into the sea. So thick had been the ice sheet and so profuse were its melting waters that all the oceans of the earth began to overflow.

Off the Golden Gate the rising sea crept slowly up on the low delta, engulfing it inch by inch. For seventy-five thousand years the great thaw continued. Eventually the delta was covered by the rising sea; by 150,000 B.C. the river's mouth was again at the Golden Gate, and the ocean entered the narrow river canyon. The birth of the bay had begun.

Possibly there was some subsidence of the land which played a part in the bay's growth. But from whatever combination of causes the salty waters slowly moved in through the strait, century after century, past the narrows where one day the Golden Gate Bridge would stand, past the rocky peak which would be called Alcatraz. The encroaching sea spread from the river channel to the surrounding valley, creating tidal marshes, then flooding the marshes themselves until they became sea bottom. Plant and animal life retreated before the rising flood. The ridges across the valley floor were partly or totally surrounded by water and became peninsulas or islands. But sometime before the bay reached its present size, possibly around 100,000 B.C., its growth ceased.

The weather had entered another of its inexplicable cycles. The air grew cooler. Again in the Sierra and throughout the northern hemisphere the ice sheets began to form. Instead of releasing their waters to the rivers, the mountains retained them in snowbanks and ice sheets. As a result the seas began to recede again. The bay gradually drained out of the valley and the river again flowed through the Golden Gate to the ocean. Trees grew and animals grazed again on what had been bay bottom.

Once more, however, the cold cycle ran itself out, and by 25,000 B.C. the thaw resumed. The sea came in through the Gate, rose in the valley, surrounded the ridges, created islands, and spread a sheet of water across the valley floor for fifty miles. By possibly 10,000 B.C.—only yesterday, as geologic time goes—the invading salt water had moved through the Berkeley Hills at Carquinez canyon and spread to the lowlands of the Central Valley beyond. San Francisco Bay was of age, ready for the coming of man.

WINTER

As the only sea-level break in the Coast Range and thus the meeting place of continental and oceanic air masses, the bay is a superb show place for winter cloud pageants. Here are great open spaces like those in the flat deserts of the Southwest; here is a rim of mountains interrupting the movements of air, providing updrafts and downdrafts for cloud formation; here, above all, is a gemlike surface to reflect and transmute the cloud lights and shadows as they move through the skies above it.

Early on a winter morning a giant strato-cumulus towers ten thousand feet above its base on Tamalpais. Within its billowy terraces are depths and hollows and swelling domes of pearl and alabaster, limned by shade, slowly separating and merging into new forms. The entire structure is reflected in the bay, a billowy Taj Mahal mirrored in the still waters.

Above the eastern hills from Richmond to Berkeley to Oakland to Hayward is a long cloud wall that hangs like an immense wave about to break. Its trough and body are shaded; its foaming crest gleams with dazzling brilliance from the sun behind it and trails long banners of white spindrift. It hovers poised over the cities and hills of the east shore, dwarfing them beneath its immensity, obscuring them in its shadow, rolling almost imperceptibly and shattering at the crest into fantastic shapes.

After an hour the wave begins to disintegrate; sunlight streams through its rifts and sends brilliant spangles across the water, silhouetting the Bay Bridge. In front of the cloud the bay is a milky white; boats and their wakes are black and one-dimensional.

Above the water and around the shores the cloud forms continue to grow and shift and evolve in upward-expanding shapes as if the bay itself, to transcend its own flatness, were giving birth to vapory children of light.

3

The Drake Mystery

The discovery of San Francisco Bay was one of the most confused episodes in New World history. For more than two hundred years unnumbered mariners sailed past its entrance unaware of its existence. Like California itself, the bay was named before it was found. And the question of who made the actual discovery is a mystery not yet completely unraveled. New clues are still turning up, provoking newspaper headlines and new volleys of controversy.

Until almost the turn of the present century it was generally assumed that the bay had been discovered in 1579 by the explorer, naval strategist, adventurer and one of the most colorful buccaneers who ever sailed the seas—Francis Drake.

Subsequently a new theory came to be widely accepted: Drake had not sailed his *Golden Hinde* into San Francisco Bay after all but had missed the Golden Gate entirely and entered instead a smaller coastal indentation, some thirty miles north, now known as Drake's Bay. The honor and credit for making the discovery thereupon went from the English to the Spanish, from Drake to an explorer by land who arrived nearly two centuries later, Gaspar de Portolá.

Then in 1936 occurred an almost unbelievable episode that seemed tentatively to restore the glory to Drake and to Britain.

Drake's Calling Card   One warm Sunday afternoon in the early summer of 1936 a twenty-five-year-old department store employee named Beryle Shinn, while picnicking on a hill at the shore of the bay near San Quentin, accidentally unearthed a rectangular brass plate about eight inches long. It was caked with dirt but appeared to be the right size to cover a hole in the floor of his old car. He tossed the plate into the back seat.

Some weeks later he got the plate out to make the repair job and scrubbed some of the dirt off. As he did so, he noticed what appeared to be some illegible writing scratched deep in its surface. In the lower right-hand corner was a small hole.

A friend of Shinn's looked at the plate, studied the writing, and with sudden amazement made out a single word at the bottom: "DRAKE." He remembered a history class at the University of California taught by Professor Herbert E. Bolton, who jokingly used to tell his students to be on the lookout for a brass plate supposedly left by Drake nearly four centuries ago to mark his visit to California.

Quickly he phoned Bolton. The professor was skeptical but agreed to look at the plate. He examined it closely, and with mounting excitement he deciphered the words:

BEE IT KNOWNE UNTO ALL MEN
BY THESE PRESENTS
June 17, 1579
By the Grace of God and in the Name of Herr Majesty

Queen Elizabeth of England and Herr Successors Forever
I Take Possession of This Kingdome Whose King and People Freely Resigne Their Right and Title in the Whole
Land unto Herr Majesties Keepeing. Now Named by Me
an to Bee Knowne unto All Men as Nova Albion.

G. Francis Drake

The historian quickly turned to a copy of the record of
Drake's voyage made by the ship's chaplain, Francis
Fletcher:

> . . . Our Generall caused to be set up a monument of our
> being there, as also of her majesties and succesors right
> and title to that kingdom, namely a plate of brasse, fast
> nailed to a great firme post, whereon is engraven her
> graces name, and the yeare of our arrivall there; and of
> free giving up of the province and kingdome, both by the
> king and people into her majesties hands; together with
> her highness picture and armes in a peice of sixpence cur-
> rent English monie, shewing itselfe by a hole made of pur-
> pose through the plate, underneath likewise was engraven
> the name of our Generall.

The similarities were striking. Bolton even found that the
hole in Shinn's plate was just the size to hold an Elizabethan
sixpence.

But doubts still persisted in the historian's mind. Could the
plate have been a forgery? He sent it to the man regarded as
the nation's foremost expert in electrochemistry, Dr. Colin C.
Fink, of Columbia University, who subjected it to exacting
tests. From microscopic examination of the metal, the patina
covering it, and analysis of the mineralized plant tissue in the
coin slot Fink and his associates deduced that the plate was
undoubtedly of Elizabethan origin and manufacture.

"It is our opinion," they concluded, "that the brass plate
examined by us is the genuine Drake plate."

Did the discovery of the plate on the shores of San Francisco Bay prove that Drake had actually landed there? Not necessarily, Bolton concluded, but it certainly reopened the possibility that he had done so.

"It is conceivable," Bolton said, "that investigation may prove that the plate was discovered on the very site where Drake nailed it to the 'firme post' and that the beach at the foot of the hill was the very spot where he careened and repaired the *Golden Hinde*."

For a time it seemed as if the history books might have to be rewritten again, renaming Drake as the bay's discoverer. Then came a strange postscript to the story of the plate. A chauffeur named William Caldeira said that he had found this same plate some three years earlier near Drake's Bay. Unaware of its significance, he had kept it in his car for a time, then had thrown it out. As he recalled, he had tossed it into a meadow near the site of Shinn's picnic.

There were numerous skeptics regarding Caldeira's story. Some wondered how he could be certain that the plate was the same one. And how could it have been moved from the meadow where he said he had discarded it to the hilltop where Shinn found it, several hundred yards away? Others refused to believe the tale at all, claiming that Caldeira had simply invented it for publicity. But partisans of Drake's Bay hailed Caldeira's story as proof that the English explorer had landed there after all, rather than in San Francisco Bay.

The Harbor of the Golden Hinde   Historians trying to track down answers to the puzzle of Drake's landing pored over the available documents for further clues as to whether the great privateer could have sailed this coast without discovering and entering the Golden Gate.

One item was significant: A great many Spanish navigators before and after Drake—including those of the Cabrillo expedition of 1542 and the captains of the galleons sailing periodically from Manila to Mexico—undoubtedly sailed past the Golden Gate without ever suspecting its existence. How did they miss it? The most bizarre theory—in vogue after the great San Francisco earthquake of 1906—was that the Gate and the bay had not existed at all in the days of the early explorers but had been opened by a sudden cataclysm late in the eighteenth century. A more plausible explanation is that the bay entrance is often hidden by fog banks and even on clear days is not readily visible from some distance at sea.

On his southbound voyage the summer of 1579, however, Drake was carefully exploring the California shoreline for a snug harbor in which to careen and repair his *Golden Hinde* for a westward journey across the Pacific—a characteristically daring venture, in view of the fact that such a voyage had been made only once before in history—by the Magellan expedition. Fletcher's journal of the voyage states that the ship "fell with a convenient and fit harborough," at a point variously given as 38° and 38° 30′ latitude. The 38th parallel passes through both Drake's Bay and San Francisco Bay.

Fletcher mentions the bleak countryside, the "nipping cold," and the "thicke mists and most stynkinge fogges." Drake and his men anchored the ship close to the beach near the foot of a high hill, went ashore, and set up a camp, fortified by a stone wall.

Curious Indians swarmed to see the bearded white men and proved almost embarrassingly friendly. They were fascinated by the religious services and at each pause raised a cry that sounded to the Englishmen like "Amen!" They then staged a ceremony of their own during which the chief, Hioh, came forward and placed a "crown" on the brow of the surprised Drake. In claiming the land for Queen Elizabeth, Drake named it Nova Albion "in respect of the white banks and cliffes, which lie toward the sea," resembling the cliffs of

Dover. Drake's Bay is bounded by white cliffs—the most decisive piece of evidence in favor of the supposition that he landed there. But there is also a white cliff on the south shore of the Golden Gate; Fort Point was originally called by the Spaniards "Punta del Cantil Blanco," Point of the Steep White Cliff.

The day after leaving the harbor the *Golden Hinde* stopped at the Farallones and the crew secured some seal meat. This incident is evidence used by those who claim the *Golden Hinde* was anchored in San Francisco Bay. The main islands are only twenty miles from Drake's Bay—hardly a day's journey—but about thirty-five miles from any good anchorage inside the Golden Gate against prevailing winds —a much more likely distance for the ship to have sailed in a day.

The *Golden Hinde* sailed on across the Pacific and eventually reached England, where Drake was knighted by Queen Elizabeth for his history-making voyage. He presented the Queen with his logbook, which undoubtedly contained data identifying the California harbor more specifically.

What the Queen did with the log is unknown; it has never been seen since. If it is ever found, it will probably shed light on another intriguing possibility. There is a legend, perpetuated in a short story by Bret Harte but unsubstantiated in any of the known records, that in order to lighten his ship for the Pacific crossing Drake buried part of his heavy cargo of treasure looted from Spanish galleons. The buccaneer never returned to California, and the treasure, according to the legend, still remains buried beneath the sandy shore where he landed.

Just sixteen years after the *Golden Hinde* left California, the Spanish viceroy in Mexico ordered Sebastián Cermeño to make a survey of the California coast. Cermeño left Manila in command of one of the regular galleons, followed the usual route eastward across the Pacific, and hit the California coast in the vicinity of Cape Mendocino. Like Drake he sailed south along the coast, looking for a harbor which would shelter his ship, the *San Agustín*, from the heavy sea and strong winds.

He found sanctuary in a large bay sheltered from the ocean by a rocky peninsula. The expedition remained there a month. Because of Cermeño's careful exploration and precise description of the body of water and its large estuary there is no doubt that he landed in what is today known as Drake's Bay. Partisans of this harbor as Drake's landing place argue that, if Cermeño found this bay the best available anchorage, it is probable that Drake, impelled by the same considerations, would have made the same finding.

On the other hand, Cermeño found no sign of Drake's visit. The Indians gave no indication of any previous encounter with Europeans, and Drake's fortification was not discovered despite a thorough exploration. Cermeño named this harbor "La Bahía de San Francisco" for St. Francis of Assisi—a fact responsible for much of the confusion of future historians regarding identification of the bays in this area.

In spite of the shelter afforded by the peninsula a great wind roaring up from the southeast drove the *San Agustín* ashore from its anchorage, wrecked it completely, and scattered its cargo. Cermeño and his crew had to complete their journey down the coast in an open boat. They passed inside the Farallones but failed to sight the Golden Gate.

An even more thorough survey of the California coast than Cermeño's was made seven years later by Sebastián Vizcaíno, whose special mission was to find a good port for the Manila galleons. Unlike Drake and Cermeño, who had come southward along the coast, Vizcaíno sailed directly north from Mexico. His greatest single discovery was the bay of Monterey. Shrewdly he named it in honor of the Mexican viceroy who had sent him on the trip, and he wrote a glowing description of it that should qualify him for honorary membership in the California Chamber of Commerce.

Sailing on north from Monterey, he spotted a great headland jutting into the ocean. His pilot, Bolaños, who had been with Cermeño, recognized it as the point enclosing Cermeño's Bahía de San Francisco, today's Drake's Bay. Vizcaíno probably headed directly for that promontory, which he subsequently named Point Reyes, crossing open water instead of making the longer trip along the coastline.

Had he hove closer to land, he doubtless would have seen the break in the shoreline marking the Golden Gate. As it was, he by-passed it, and the greatest natural harbor in the New World remained hidden behind the coastal hills for another 167 years.

Portolá's Discovery by Mistake   On a clear, cold October morning in 1769 a weary, half-starved little party of Spaniards led by Captain Gaspar de Portolá trudged up Montara Mountain high above Half Moon Bay—the first white men ever to penetrate this far by land up the Pacific coast of North America.

Gazing over the view from the peak, Portolá was puzzled. He had been searching for Monterey Bay, as described by Vizcaíno. But the coastline before him was obviously far north of Monterey. The landmarks here, named by Vizcaíno, were unmistakable: the Farallon Islands thirty miles offshore and the long headland of Point Reyes to the north, enclosing what Cermeño had named the "Bay of San Francisco."

Portolá realized that he had overshot his goal of Monterey Bay. It was time to turn back.

He decided first, however, to lay over a day or two and send scouting parties out to hunt game and perhaps find a way up the coast to Point Reyes. The scouts came back with a surprising story. A vast lake or arm of the ocean extended north as far as they could see and blocked the way to Point Reyes.

Portolá was not impressed by the discovery of the new bay, neglecting even to give it a name. He was concerned with the fact that the way to Point Reyes was not open and even more concerned that the hunters had been unsuccessful in bringing back a good supply of meat.

He remained in the area long enough to probe around the east shore of the inland sea but became discouraged about finding a land route to Point Reyes and its "Bahía de San Francisco." Famished and exhausted, he and his men turned south again. En route they ran so low on food that they had to eat their pack animals, arriving at San Diego, according to their chaplain's diary, "smelling frightfully of mules."

From the reports of Portolá and of subsequent expeditions the Spaniards assumed that this newly discovered body of water was simply an arm or estuary of the Bahía de San Francisco under Point Reyes. It was thus first known as the "Estero de San Francisco," and the confusion concerning the two bays had begun.

Map makers in England contributed further to the mix-up by assuming, as patriotic Englishmen, that "San Francisco" was obviously Spanish for "Sir Francis" Drake. When the name was transferred to the present San Francisco Bay, Drake's name went along with it as its discoverer.

But by the 1880s some historians began to have doubts. They were led by one of the West's pioneer scientists, Professor George Davidson, a brilliant, dogmatic, flowing-bearded patriarch who spoke with such authority that his opinions were seldom challenged. Carefully tracing Drake's voyage down the coast, he placed the anchorage of the *Golden Hinde* in what is now known as Drake's Bay, and more particularly

in a sheltered cove just inside the hooked eastern tip of Point
Reyes. San Francisco Bay and its entrance were not visible
from that point, Davidson argued, and Drake would have had
no reason to search farther. Surely if Drake had entered the
Golden Gate, the professor speculated, Fletcher in his eyewitness account of the voyage "would have given a graphic
description of so unique an entrance and so magnificent an
inland sea."

Davidson cited a map of Drake's California anchorage published by the Dutch cartographer Jodocus Hondius, a few
years after the voyage. The drawing has always puzzled historians. Containing neither scale nor indication of direction,
it portrays a horseshoe-shaped bay bounded on the right by
the mainland and on the left by a long narrow peninsula. In
the center a ship, presumably the *Golden Hinde*, is shown
riding at anchor, and a village is pictured on the shores.

Hondius' map, Davidson declared, bore a striking resemblance to Drake's Bay—except in one detail. On the map
alongside the outer edge of the peninsula is what appears to
be a large island, almost as long as the peninsula itself. There
is no such island at Drake's Bay or evidently anywhere else
along the California shoreline.

But off the inner tip of Point Reyes, Davidson pointed out,
there is a rock which may be taken as Hondius' island, simply
misplaced and enlarged by the map maker.

Actually, Davidson's tiny rock bears no resemblance to the
Hondius island, and the statement may be taken as evidence
that Davidson, like most people, was perfectly capable of
glossing over discrepancies in order to make the facts fit his
theory.

Nevertheless, Davidson's verdict has been generally accepted by most history writers, although there are a few who
maintain that Drake landed at Bodega Bay, twenty-two miles
farther north.

The Great Debate   The staunchest opposition to David-son's theory still comes from those who claim that the harbor under Point Reyes is far too exposed for Drake to have risked careening his ship there and that he undoubtedly anchored in the only secure harbor on the Northern California coast for a craft the size of the *Golden Hinde*—inside the Golden Gate.

Why didn't Fletcher give a "graphic description of so unique an entrance and so magnificent an inland sea"? For San Francisco partisans there are several possible answers: Such topographical data would more logically have been en-tered in Drake's lost logbook than in the chaplain's diary. Fur-ther, it is possible that the main features of the Gate were obscured by fog as the *Golden Hinde* passed through the strait. But even if Fletcher did see and describe the area in more detail, it is conceivable that this material may have been lost or deliberately omitted by the Elizabethan compilers of his writings. Such a tremendous harbor as San Francisco Bay would have been of great strategic value to imperial Britain; since Queen Elizabeth was unable to follow up Drake's dis-covery with immediate colonization, the shrewd monarch would never have given away its existence to the Spaniards by allowing details of its size and location to be published.

And so theories are built on theories in fascinating array. About once a year someone breaks into Bay Area newspapers with a new one. The amateur historians of the Drake Naviga-tors Guild maintain that the *Golden Hinde* was careened not in Drake's Bay proper but in Drake's Estero, the shallow but more protected inner harbor, which, they believe, was deeper in Drake's time. The "island" on the Hondius map was a sand bar which has since been washed away. Another amateur named Robert H. Power has published in *Pacific Discovery*, a magazine of the California Academy of Sciences, a theory that the Hondius map was actually a drawing of the sector of San Francisco Bay north and east of Angel Island: Hondius' peninsula was Tiburon and the mysterious island alongside it was Belvedere.

For many old-time Bay Area residents "Drake" is a fascinating hobby. One's favorite bay is to be defended in the same sporting spirit with which he would cheer for the football teams of Stanford or the University of California at the Big Game. Around countless firesides on long winter nights, during innumerable trans-bay ferry rides and bridge crossings, partisans of each bay have argued their claims for decades.

The truth is that no one knows where Drake anchored. The widely accepted designation of Drake's Bay as the landing needs to be replaced by a more realistic view. It is quite conceivable that Drake sailed through the Golden Gate and discovered San Francisco Bay.

It is also conceivable that he missed it entirely. Any of several theories can be plausibly defended and as plausibly attacked. The public and many historians, in their impatient desire for final answers, have tended too readily to accept without criticism the arguments of whatever theorists were able to make their guesswork sound most authoritative.

Doubtless new clues will continue to turn up for years to come. Perhaps someone wandering along an unfrequented beach will come across the remains of Drake's stone fortifications, or possibly another picnicker will find the sixpence lost from the hole in the plate of brass. Or some researcher in British archives might unearth the yellowed leaves of the lost logbook of the *Golden Hinde*, identifying the anchorage beyond doubt.

Probably there are a good many amateur sleuths who secretly hope that such a thing never happens. Drake is far more intriguing as a mystery.

SPRING'S BEGINNING

Spring comes softly to the bay. It comes with a light haze and a genial sun. After the winds and rains and sharp clear days of winter, after the low-flying clouds and the whitecaps and the sharp-limned clarity of every ship, every island, every building on the far shore, comes a period of warmth and stillness.

Mornings the bay is glassy and often enveloped in a transparent mist that obscures the horizon and is scarcely distinguishable from the water. Ships seem to move through the sky as if in a mirage. The islands and the hills of the Marin shore hang above the water like the floating landscapes of a Japanese painting.

Even at the cliffs of the Gate, where all winter the waves have pounded relentlessly, the shores are now washed by gentle swells. Everywhere the haze floats over the water, softening the outlines of rocks, of cliffs, of buildings. Even the great bridges lose some of their power and austerity and become airy and graceful and delicate in the luminous vapors of spring.

Afternoons the breeze comes in from the ocean—not the biting wind of winter that whips the water into whitecaps, but a gentle motion of air that barely ruffles the surface, yet begins to clear away the haze. By later afternoon the east shore, which all morning was nearly invisible from San Francisco, now becomes distinct again.

Then as afternoon turns to evening, the hills of the east shore begin to blaze as ten thousand windows catch the light of the setting sun—the glowing fires of a dying spring day.

4

Bay of Destiny

You always remember the first time you saw San Francisco Bay.

It comes back to you in later years with vivid intensity: the sudden, breath-taking impact of that initial moment when the great bay was first spread out before you, fresh and new and shining like a banner and a herald of things to come.

Even if you were a native of the area and grew up on these shores, it is probable that there was some single instant, on a bridge or a hilltop or some unfrequented beach, when you suddenly became conscious of the bay, when you really saw it for the first time—no longer an accustomed part of the background but a thing of beauty and power that had somehow become part of you.

Or, if you came from another part of the country, you may have seen it first from the air or from one of its highway approaches or from the deck of the Oakland ferry at sundown, when the water around you was luminous with crimson fire and vertical patterns of lights glowed from the darkening towers of San Francisco. Then, suddenly, no matter what your age, you were young, and the bay around you and the city beyond it were the future, full of great and glowing promise.

At that moment, whenever it may have been, you became a member of that company of explorers, pioneers, Argonauts, and empire builders who came to this edge of the New World when the land was young and, like you, felt a sudden blaze of exhilaration, a premonition of glory, an indefinable sense that this was a place of destiny—a giant theater for history-to-be and the place where their own private dreams would surely be fulfilled.

The Opening of the Gate   The history of San Francisco Bay can be told in terms of the people who saw—and some who failed to see—its high promise and historic destiny.

Surely Padre Crespi, Portolá's chaplain, glimpsed this destiny when he wrote in his diary: "It is a harbor such that not only the navy of our most Catholic Majesty but those of all Europe could take shelter in it."

And certainly young Juan Manuel de Ayala must have felt it when, six years after Portolá, he steered the little *San Carlos* toward the Golden Gate. Early on the morning of August 5, 1775, Ayala and his crew stood on the deck of the *San Carlos* gazing at the Golden Gate from the sea, a sight no European —with the possible exception of Drake—had ever seen. There before them was the hidden strait which navigators had passed by for two centuries. The high cliffs at the heads were in deep shadow. The waves dashed against jagged rock islands just offshore, and the bluffs funneled ominously to a gap barely a mile wide at the narrows.

In the six years since Portolá only two other land expeditions had visited the bay: Lieutenant Pedro Fages had explored along the east shore past Carquinez, and Captain Fernando de Rivera had marched up the peninsula to Point Lobos, where he had planted a cross.

No one knew whether this strait was navigable, what rocks lay just below the surface, what currents might carry a ship onto the cliffs. The men on the *San Carlos* gazed in apprehension at the boiling waters around Point Bonita, at the knife-edged rocks at Land's End, at the high, frowning escarpments towering above the water.

What lay beyond this mighty entrance? How far did this passage penetrate into the interior? Did it connect with Cermeño's "Bahía de San Francisco" under Point Reyes? Were there other outlets to the ocean?

At eight o'clock that morning Ayala sent his first mate, José Cañizares, ahead in a small boat to probe the entrance and find an anchorage for the ship. The mate and his men rowed out of sight within an hour. By that time the tide was ebbing strongly. Riverlike currents swept the little *San Carlos* and her surprised crew out to sea.

When the tide turned, Ayala cautiously approached the heads, taking soundings. Night was coming. There was a stiff breeze from the west, and Ayala made a bold decision: He would not wait for Cañizares but would make a run for it and try to find an anchorage before nightfall. Every sail on the ship was hoisted and filled by the wind, but as the *San Carlos* moved within the heads and bore down on the narrows, she was slowed almost to a standstill by the swiftly ebbing tide. Her bow pitched into the onrushing waters and threw cold flying spray into the air.

Ayala was in a predicament that was to befall many another navigator who did not calculate the fury of the strait's currents. But luckily the current began to slacken, the wind held, and the ship slowly slipped between the darkening cliffs and passed through the narrows where the giant bridge would one day rise. As the wind died, the *San Carlos* edged along the north shore and dropped an anchor in the dark.

It held fast. After two centuries, the great Gate was open.

A Welcome for the Invaders   When the sun rose from behind the Berkeley Hills the next morning, Ayala and his men beheld an unforgettable sight. They found themselves in a cove opposite a small grove of willow trees—a *sauzalito,* from which the town eventually built there took its name. Behind it the first rays of the sun were striking long-ridged Mount Tamalpais, which rose half a mile into the sky. To the south, across the strait, was the tip of a hilly peninsula where San Francisco would one day stand. And to the east the bay opened into an intriguing unexplored expanse of blue below the bordering mountains.

Cañizares and his men rowed to the anchored *San Carlos* from a beach on the south shore; they told a story of being caught in overpowering currents which had prevented them from returning to the ship the previous day.

Ayala sent Cañizares to sound Richardson Bay off Sausalito for a possible anchorage, but after an exploration the mate decided against the site because of its exposure to southeast winds and its soft bottom, in which an anchor could not take hold. Instead the vessel was moved around the tip of Belvedere to the cove at Tiburon.

As it passed Belvedere Point, the ship was hailed by Indians; they seemed friendly; and the next day Ayala sent a delegation to make cautious contact. Like those who had welcomed Drake, the natives extended the best California hospitality to the Spaniards, ushered them to their village, and spread before them a dinner of corn meal, bread, and tamales.

Later Ayala reciprocated by fêting the natives on shipboard, where they delighted their hosts by learning to speak a few words of Spanish.

The *San Carlos* finally found a good permanent anchorage across Raccoon Strait in a cove on an island Ayala named for the Virgin, Isla de Nuestra Señora de los Angeles—later shortened to Angel Island. Increasing numbers of curious Indians paddled to the cove on rafts and canoes. They stared in wonder when the padre said a thanksgiving Mass on the island and the Spaniards shouted nine times: "*Viva el rey!*"

Little did the natives realize what history had in store for their bay. Life on its shores was easy. The waters were full of fish for the taking; the fields and hills were abundant with rabbits and other small game. The bay tribes were among the most primitive on the continent. They had developed only the crudest of cultures. They wore little or no clothing and did not even make pottery but relied on tule baskets and lived in shelters made of poles tied together. They had lived in the area probably four thousand years without change.

Yet until the coming of white men they were healthy, strong, and apparently happy; they bore no malice toward the bearded strangers who came to their shores, displaying naïve friendliness and good will. They could scarcely anticipate that Ayala and his men were the precursors of an invasion which would mean their near extinction as a race.

The Spaniards went about their work, themselves oblivious to the long-run consequences of their visit. They probed the bay's various arms, following the windings of its shoreline, and penetrated through Carquinez in the north and to the edge of the Santa Clara Valley in the south, making soundings, noting beaches and harbors, and preparing a crude chart—the first survey of the bay.

The exploration finally settled one vexing question. This vast, landlocked arm of the sea was not connected by water with the harbor under Point Reyes, as had been supposed. Moreover, it was vastly superior to Cermeño's Bahía de San Francisco and clearly the great west-coast port the explorers had been hoping to find. From Ayala's voyage on the name San Francisco was attached to this bay, and the harbor under Point Reyes, which had figured prominently in the earlier explorations, was gradually forgotten; even today—renamed for Drake—it remains isolated and almost uninhabited, bypassed by time.

At the end of a month Ayala's job was done. He weighed anchor early in the morning and sailed outward on the tide. But again the *San Carlos* was caught in the swirling currents between the great cliffs, and this time she did not escape so easily. She was driven onto a rock near Point Cavallo on the north shore, and her rudder was damaged. Ayala put her into Horseshoe Bay just inside the point while the damage was repaired. On September 18, 1775, the unwieldy little *San Carlos* sailed out the Golden Gate and into history.

Anza, Empire Builder   At about the same time that a little band of revolutionists on the opposite shore of the continent was planning to proclaim the right of all men to life, liberty, and the pursuit of happiness, an event of decisive importance took place on San Francisco Bay.

On a clear day in spring seven men mounted a rise near the tip of the peninsula and sighted the inland sea. They stopped there, staring in wonder. Padre Pedro Font wrote in his diary: "And there we saw a prodigy of nature which it is not easy to describe."

The leader of the group was the soldier, explorer, colonizer, and first of the West's empire builders, Juan Bautista de Anza. It was Anza who first saw clearly the possibilities of this bay as a center of civilization.

Anza had performed the feat—unequaled in pioneer annals —of leading an expedition of 240 men, women, and children some sixteen hundred miles from Mexico to the Spanish settlement at Monterey. There he left the group to rest while he scouted ahead for the best site to plant a colony on the shores of the Bay of St. Francis.

The point from which Anza and his party first sighted the bay was the high mesa where the Presidio now stands. He named the southern promontory of the strait (now Fort Point) "Punta del Cantil Blanco," Point of the Steep White Cliff—possibly the same cliff which two hundred years before had reminded Drake of Dover.

Font wrote with earthy accuracy, "The cliff is very high and perpendicular, so that from it one can spit into the sea." He also observed "the spouting of whales, a shoal of dolphins or tunny fish, sea otter, and sea lions." There, on the point of the Cantil Blanco, Anza set up a cross overlooking the bay's entrance.

The excitement of Anza and his men at the possibilities of this place was vividly recorded by the padre:

> The port of San Francisco is a marvel of nature, and might well be called the harbor of harbors . . . This mesa affords a most delightful view, for from it one sees a large part of the port and its islands, as far as the other side, the mouth of the harbor, and of the sea all that the sight can take in as far as beyond the Farallones.

The sense of an awaiting destiny that impresses nearly everyone who beholds the bay for the first time filled Font and Anza with wonder, and they envisioned its great future:

> Although in all my travels [wrote the padre] I saw very good sites and beautiful country, I saw none which pleased me as much as this. And I think that if it could be well settled like Europe, there would not be anything more beautiful . . . for it has all the conveniences desired,

by land as well as by sea, with that harbor so remarkable
and so spacious that in it may be established shipyards,
docks and anything that may be wished. This mesa the
commander designated as the site for the new settlement
and fort which were to be established on this harbor.

A short distance down the inner shore of the peninsula,
they came upon "a beautiful arroyo which, because it was the
Friday of Sorrows [the Friday before Palm Sunday] we called
the Arroyo de los Dolores." Up the arroyo, or lagoon, the soil
seemed good, and Anza decided it was the best place to build
one of the two Franciscan missions which Spanish authorities
had ordered established in the bay area. Mission Dolores, now
restored, still stands on the site Anza designated.

By a twist of fate the actual establishment of both the
Presidio and the Mission was left to Anza's lieutenant, José
Joaquín Moraga, after the commander had returned to Mexico, and it was Moraga who led Anza's settlers from Monterey
to San Francisco. The Presidio was founded on September 17
and Mission Dolores dedicated on October 8, 1776.

Anza and Moraga had planted on the shores of the great
bay the seeds of empire.

Idyl on the Bay   The seeds were a long time sprouting.
Anza's colonists, lacking their leader's vision of cities on the
bay, subsequently left the windy sand hills of the peninsula
and established the village of San José forty miles to the south
in the fertile Santa Clara Valley. There, too, the second mission was built. This left on the peninsula only Mission Dolores tended by the padres and their Indian converts, and a
small military garrison at the Presidio.

The age of Spanish supremacy in the New World was on
the wane, and if the complacent proconsuls of Madrid were
unable to think and act in terms of this bay's destiny, there

were others who could. As the existence of this superb body of water and potential base of empire became known in the other capitals of Europe, covetous eyes began to look in this direction.

The first non-Spanish navigator to enter the bay after Ayala was an energetic young spiritual heir of Drake, Captain George Vancouver, who sailed his British sloop of war, H.M.S. *Discovery,* into the Golden Gate on a windy November night in 1792, failed to sight what he assumed would be "the Spanish town of San Francisco," and anchored a few miles to the east in a cove named Yerba Buena, for the good herb or wild mint which grew in abundance there.

When later he located the Presidio and Mission, he was surprised at the lack of a more substantial settlement, and noted significantly in a report to his superiors the decrepitude of the Spanish colony in contrast with the great natural advantages of the bay.

An even more avid interest in the bay was shown by representatives of another empire, considerably closer than the British. The Russian Bear was spread halfway around the world from Europe to Alaska, and the Czar's fur trappers were reaping a rich harvest in pelts along the northwest coast of the American continent. In 1806 a shrewd emissary of the Czar sailed south from the Russian outpost at Sitka, entered the Golden Gate, and played the leading role in a poignant idyl resembling the plot of Puccini's *Madama Butterfly.*

Nicolai Petrovich Rezanov was an ambitious young diplomat who came to the California settlement with a double objective—to secure an emergency food supply for the hungry Russian colonists at Sitka and to arrange for regular trade between California and Alaska. But he faced formidable obstacles. The Spanish crown, wary of Russian imperialism, had ordered that all non-Spanish ships be barred from California ports.

Rezanov's continental charm, however, won not only the esteem of José Argüello, the Presidio *comandante*, but the affection of his sixteen-year-old daughter, Concepción. Historians have long debated whether Rezanov was actually in love with the dark-eyed beauty or was hardheartedly using her to achieve his diplomatic ends. In any event, despite the difference in religion, the family finally agreed to a tentative betrothal pending approval by the Pope. Rezanov was to return to Sitka with a shipload of food for the settlers there, proceed across Siberia to St. Petersburg to place before the Czar a proposal for Russian-Spanish trade on the Pacific coast, then go to Rome and ask the Pope for approval of the marriage—a plan which would require two years.

Rezanov never returned to San Francisco. Concepción waited year after year, turning down all suitors, devoting herself to ministering to the poor and the sick. Many years after Rezanov's ship had disappeared beyond the horizon she learned the truth: Her lover had died on the three-thousand-mile trek across the wilds of Siberia. She took the veil, became Sister María Domínica, and died in the Dominican Convent at Benicia in 1857.

In a report written before his death, Rezanov revealed that the *señorita* was not the only feature of California that excited his admiration. While wooing the maiden he was also looking over her shoulder at the great bay itself.

Rezanov may or may not have envisioned, as some historians have suggested, the spires and domes of a Russian city on this bay; but it is clear that he did contemplate the extension of the Russian domain south toward this bay from its colonies in Alaska. He wrote to his superior in St. Petersburg:

> Your excellency perhaps will laugh at my far-reaching plans, but I am certain that they will prove exceedingly profitable ventures, and if we had men and means, even

without any great sacrifice on the part of the treasury, all
this country [north of the Golden Gate] could be made
a corporeal part of the Russian Empire . . .

Prize of Empire   Although Rezanov died before he could
present his proposal in person to the Czar, it was perhaps
in response to his enthusiastic report on this region that the
Russians six years later established Fort Ross as a trapping
and trading port near the mouth of what came to be called the
Russian River, sixty miles north of the Golden Gate. Subsequently they set up a colony at Bodega Bay and even established an outpost on the Farallones, twenty-seven miles
off Point Bonita.

If Rezanov had lived to return to San Francisco—or if Russia had possessed more men of his caliber and ambition to
follow up on his bold dreams—the Czar might have seized
the great prize of the Pacific coast and planted his own empire on the shores of this bay. Doubtless the history of California would then have taken some interesting turns.

But another destiny was waiting instead. The Russian Empire, like that of Spain, was spread too thin and lacked the
vitality to grasp its opportunities. A younger, more vigorous
people was moving in this direction.

One of the first of this breed to sail into the harbor was
Richard Henry Dana in 1835. In *Two Years Before the Mast*
the Yankee noted that a Russian brig from Sitka was the only
other vessel in the bay. He gathered wood for his ship from
the forests on Angel Island and watched the "hundreds and
hundreds of red deer . . . great numbers of which overrun
the islands and hills of San Francisco Bay."

Two days after Christmas, Dana's *Pilgrim* hoisted anchor
and headed for home:

> We sailed down this magnificent bay with a light wind,
> the tide, which was running out, carrying us at the rate

of four or five knots. It was a fine day . . . We passed
directly under the high cliff on which the presidio is built,
and stood into the middle of the bay, from whence we
could see small bays making up into the interior, large and
beautifully wooded islands, and the mouths of several
small rivers.

With Yankee foresight Dana added:

> If California ever becomes a prosperous country, this bay
> will be the center of its prosperity. The abundance of
> wood and water; the extreme fertility of its shores; the ex-
> cellence of its climate, which is as near to being perfect
> as any in the world; and its facilities for navigation, af-
> fording the best anchoring-grounds in the whole western
> coast of America—all fit it for a place of great importance.

Dana noted how little the Spaniards and Mexicans had
accomplished. More than a half century after their first settlement here he could see only their scattered adobe structures
at the Presidio and the Mission. Significantly, the only other
building visible on the bay's shores was a "shanty of rough
boards put up by a man named Richardson, who was doing a
little trading between the vessels and the Indians."

William A. Richardson had left a British ship and become
a citizen of California. After Dana's visit he expanded his
small trade into a prosperous commercial operation, running
a trans-bay ferry, raising cattle, and trading with the Yankee
ships which increasingly began to call at the port. Richardson's shanty was not at the Presidio but around the corner on
the east side of the peninsula in Yerba Buena Cove and thus
the first building of what was to become the village of Yerba
Buena.

It was increasingly evident by this time that the Mexicans,
who had achieved their independence from Spain in 1821,
held only a faltering grip on this bay. They took no further
steps to colonize, and their only fortification was the crum-

bling Castillo de San Joaquín on Fort Point, so feeble that a discharge of its cannons would shake it to its base and crack its walls.

The Hudson's Bay Company, advance guard of the British Empire, established a branch at Yerba Buena. Even the Russians at Fort Ross flouted Mexican authority by ignoring orders to leave California and defiantly pursued seals and sea otters into the bay itself. The young giant of a nation on the east coast of this continent was stretching its limbs in answer to the call of Manifest Destiny. Yankee whalers began to drop anchor for wood and water in the bay off Sausalito, avoiding the display of their colors in order not to offend the Mexican *comandante* at the Presidio, who had his orders to keep all foreign vessels out. Andrew Jackson, symbol of the West, was in the White House, and demonstrated his awareness of the ripe prize on the Pacific coast by offering to buy this bay and its hinterland from the Mexicans for $3,500,000. His negotiations fell through, but the overture had been played and the stage was set for the main drama.

The Conquest   Onto that stage, with a bow toward the footlights, strode a flamboyant young man fully conscious of his role as an empire builder and playing the part with zest. His name was John Charles Frémont, and he entered the California scene with a flourish which was characteristically dramatic but nevertheless superbly appropriate.

Like many others coming to this place Frémont was gripped by a vision of the future. He saw the establishment of towering cities on this wild shore. He envisioned processions of ships coming and going on long trade routes to Asia. Like the ancient harbor of Byzantium at the crossroads between Europe and Asia, this too would surely become a center of world commerce. For the mighty portals giving entrance to this harbor Frémont conceived an inspired name—Golden Gate.

"I gave [it] the name Chrysopylae, or Golden Gate," he later wrote, "for the same reason that the harbor of Byzantium was called Chrysoceras or Golden Horn."

Never was a name bestowed more prophetically. Even Frémont could not know that within a few years hundreds of ships would pour through this Gate in history's greatest gold rush.

But he did know that this land was rich, that this bay was its natural capital, and that its Mexican warders were amiable but impotent. The bay and its magnificent hinterland were clearly destined to be the western bulwark of the United States of America. With somewhat more finesse than that customarily shown by conquerors Frémont reached out to pick the golden plum.

As a United States Army officer in command of a detachment of Americans ostensibly making a topographical survey, he could not take direct action on his own initiative. Early in 1846, however, he surreptitiously organized a revolt of a group of Americans at Sonoma, near the bay's north shore. Carefully avoiding direct contact with Frémont, they tore down the Mexican flag, ran up a banner of their own with a grizzly bear as its symbol, and proclaimed the Bear Flag Republic.

Frémont was soon able to intervene openly under the pretense of "protecting" the revolutionists. After a brief and easily victorious skirmish at San Rafael against a handful of Mexican troops he rode south to Sausalito and there borrowed a boat from the captain of an American ship. In the gray light before dawn Frémont and twelve of his men rowed across the Golden Gate toward El Castillo de San Joaquín. As they approached the shore, the captain thought he heard the sound of horses galloping at full speed toward Yerba

Buena. The Americans jumped ashore, climbed the bluff to the old fort, and proceeded to spike El Castillo's rusty cannons. The ghostly horsemen did not reappear. The place was deserted. The conquest completed, Frémont returned to Sonoma and proclaimed the independence of California.

A few days later in Yerba Buena Cove, a company of sailors and marines under the command of Captain John B. Montgomery marched ashore from the United States sloop of war *Portsmouth* to the sound of a fife and drum and ran up the Stars and Stripes over the town square, now Portsmouth Plaza. It was July 8, 1846. The United States and Mexico had gone to war below the Rio Grande, and Montgomery's orders came from Washington via Commodore John Drake Sloat, who had occupied California's capital at Monterey.

The Mexicans were amazed at the dynamic energy of the conquering Americans. General José Castro told his countrymen: "These Americans are so contriving that some day they will build ladders to touch the sky, and once in the heavens they will change the whole face of the universe and even the color of the stars."

The great prize had been taken by men who were riding with destiny.

City of Gold   The first thing the Americans changed was the name of the village on the peninsula's inner cove. Yerba Buena acquired the more dignified title of the bay around it—San Francisco. More ships began to anchor there, and the population grew steadily for a couple of years until it reached about eight hundred. Then, with scarcely any warning, the newly named town exploded into a fury of activity unparalleled before or since.

James Marshall had sighted the fateful gleam in the tailrace at Sutter's mill in the Sierra foothills. Sam Brannan, after shrewdly stocking his store near Sacramento with mining supplies, strode through the streets of San Francisco waving a bottle of gold dust and booming: "Gold! Gold from the American River!" It was the voice heard around the world.

On February 28, 1849, a pennant-bedecked, thousand-ton paddle-wheel steamer, the *California*, plowed through the waters of the Golden Gate packed to the funnel with the first boatload of forty-niners. A yell went up from the deck, and an answering shout echoed from the shore as the vessel rounded Telegraph Hill. Warships in the harbor boomed salutes. Small boats trailed alongside. Passengers of the *California* jammed to the rails, scrambled with each other and with members of the crew to be the first to get ashore.

In the months to come the *California* was followed by more ships, first by the dozen, then by the hundred, each loaded to the danger point—and often beyond it—with excited gold seekers. They had sung, as they came:

> "I soon shall be in San Francisco
> And then I'll look all 'round,
> And when I see the gold lumps there
> I'll pick them off the ground.
> I'll scrape the mountains clean, my boys,
> I'll drain the rivers dry,
> A pocket full of rocks bring home,
> So brothers, don't you cry."

Attribute it to greed or avarice, to love of adventure or simply the urge to do better, the fact remains that the Gold Rush was the symbol of the American dream of opportunity. All bets were off; restraints and social distinctions were swept away. All men, in that first rush to the Mother Lode, were equal; they were equally privileged to use their muscle and ingenuity and enterprise in looking for the best claims, in panning the most gold from the Sierra creeks.

They swarmed ashore in San Francisco, looked for a temporary room or a campsite, slogged along the muddy streets, and inquired about equipment and the way to the "mines." Some got pack mules for the overland trek to the foothills; others bought passage on river boats to Sacramento.

As ship crews deserted their vessels and headed for the mountains, Yerba Buena Cove became a forest of masts. Hundreds of hulks lay abandoned. Some of them were used as warehouses, offices, or public buildings. One became the city jail. Around others the land was filled in, and they became a permanent part of the city.

As waterfront lots became increasingly valuable, energetic promoters bought beachside pieces of the bay, dumped dirt into them, reared buildings, and left the former waterfront owners high and dry. Eventually the cove was completely filled in. The city itself was spreading not only into the bay but in every direction, across the hills and sand dunes. San Francisco was the capital of all this Western land, terminus of the sea lanes bringing the Argonauts and the food and equipment to supply them. Bayard Taylor wrote for the New York *Tribune:*

> Of all the marvellous phases of the history of the Present, the growth of San Francisco is the one which will most tax the belief of the Future. Its parallel was never known, and shall never be beheld again. I speak only of what I saw with my own eyes . . . Like the magic seed of the Indian juggler, which grew, blossomed and bore fruit before the eyes of the spectators, San Francisco seemed to have accomplished in a day the growth of half a century.

"Emporium of a New World"   Richard Henry Dana returned to the bay twenty-four years after his original visit and could scarcely believe his eyes. In place of Richardson's lone shack in Yerba Buena Cove he saw "the city of San

Francisco, with its storehouses, towers and steeples; its court-houses, theaters and hospitals . . . its wharves and harbor with their thousand-ton clipper ships, more in number than London or Liverpool sheltered that day, itself one of the capitals of the American Republic, and the sole emporium of a new world, the awakened Pacific . . ."

Like the land at the tip of the peninsula, the bay itself had come alive with traffic. Where a few years before no boat had ruffled the surface except for Indian rafts and an occasional visiting ship, the water was furrowed with the wakes of fleets of vessels—ferryboats to Sausalito, Oakland, and other shores; river steamers en route to Sacramento; freighters and passenger ships from the ports of the world.

Of all those who sailed into the Golden Gate dreaming of wealth most of those whose visions came true made their fortunes not by panning gold but by selling food, clothes, and equipment to those who did. And the real significance of the Gold Rush was not in the amount of gold taken out of the ground but in the economic chain reaction it set off.

If the miners needed tools, other men needed lumber to build the factories to make the tools. Giant log rafts from the forests of the Coast Range were towed through the bay. The lumbermen in turn needed saws and axes. Farmers needed plows to grow the wheat to feed the miners—and the lumbermen and the makers of picks and shovels and saws and plows.

So the ships sailed into the great bay in ever-increasing numbers—the clippers, the square-riggers, the steamers—long after the Gold Rush was over. There were many kinds of "gold" in California's hills and cities and fertile valleys: the gold of its long fields of grain ripening in the summer heat; the green gold of its lettuce; the black gold of oil; the golden warmth of its sun; the clear gold of its flowing waters; the white gold of its cotton; the red and purple gold of its grapes.

Each kind of gold brought its own Argonauts, who crossed the Sierra from the East or sailed into the Golden Gate, each with his own personal hope of opportunity and fortune, each seeing in this bay the promise of fulfillment. More than a century after the first forty-niners sailed through the Gate, the modern Argonauts continued to arrive in ever-larger waves, and an even greater destiny seemed to await this place as the tides of history moved westward.

SPRING'S END

Toward the end of spring, in the warmth of late May, comes the first hint of summer.

It may come with a bass voice, as the sound of a single foghorn early in the morning, when the city is already warm from the rising sun. You look down in the Gate, and there over the water is a puff of white, a wisp of vapor moving across the surface like a long thin finger.

You look west, watch the sinuous white vapor come from under the bridge, from far to the west, where it first enveloped the Mile Rock lighthouse and set the big voice bellowing its warning to ships in mid-channel.

Out over Ocean Beach hang low clouds of vapor, not a fog bank yet, but a discontinuous line, like smoke from intermittent fires. The May sun is starting to warm the air over the ocean; the spring breeze is beginning to drive the cur-

rents before it; the cold water meets the warm air and cools it off, condensing its moisture into visible form.

Lighthouse keepers along the coast, from St. George Reef to Point Bonita to Point Conception, watch it and make ready to set off the great horns. Ship pilots see the chunks of vapor drift across the bay and anticipate, before long, mornings of navigating through the fog by guesswork and intuition. But now in May the smoky vapor born of the ocean depths and the countercyclonic winds of the Northern Hemisphere has not yet come to maturity, is still merely an anticipation. By an hour or two before noon the puffs of vapor will evaporate, and the long billowy line of mist over the beach will be burned off by the warm sun.

But summer has sent out its advance guard, and you know, then, that spring is nearly over.

5

Flood and Flow

The veteran captain eased his trans-bay Key Route ferry into its covered slip at the Oakland pier, just as he had been doing regularly, precisely, and without incident year after year. This time, however—a rainy morning in December of 1914— his attention was caught by an odd scraping noise that was not part of the usual cacophony of groaning timbers that accompanied the business of docking.

The sound came from overhead. The vessel safely moored, he peered out of the pilothouse. The flagpole was scraping the roof of the shed.

It hardly seemed likely that the pole would have grown in the hour since his last trip, and the possibilities of the shed roof having been lowered were even more remote. It could only mean that the boat was riding a record high tide, far higher than the published tide tables called for, higher than any previous tide in memory. And the water was still rising.

The incident dramatized a significant fact: Although the bay seems motionless when viewed from afar, actually it is always moving, vertically and horizontally, in ways that are never completely predictable. Even when it appears calm, its tranquil surface conceals water movements of tremendous magnitude and force. Never for two consecutive seconds is it ·exactly the same size or shape. Never at any one moment is it quite the same bay that it was the moment before.

Just as the light on its surface responds to the changes in the sky above it, so its rhythmic tides and currents are reactions to physical forces originating beyond its shores. It is a sensitive instrument recording events far distant in time and space, responding in complex ways to the influences of the solar system, the wind and weather, the changes in the pressure of the atmosphere and the movements of the crust of the earth.

The ferrymen were forced to lower their flagpoles on that December morning in 1914 not simply because of some local phenomenon but because of the activities of Mother Lode gold miners a half century previously; the seasonal depth of the Sierra snow pack; the temperature of the air over Northern California; the power of a storm sweeping in from the Gulf of Alaska; the relative positions of the sun, moon, and earth; and the eccentricities of the earth's satellite in its orbit.

The Pattern of Currents   The movements of the bay are direct responses to the two mighty forces whose impact first brought it into being—the ocean and the river. Of the two the ocean is primary.

Along the California coast the Pacific rises and falls twice daily. Outside the Golden Gate the rising tide builds up between the heads at Point Bonita and Point Lobos, funnels into the strait, and pours its concentrated force through the narrows at the bridge. Then it fans out to the farthest parts of the bay in an intricate pattern of currents and counter-currents, lifting fishing boats and ocean liners at their wharves, carrying away the wastes of the shoreline cities, scouring the bottom channels, transporting billions of organisms from microscopic plankton to whales, furnishing a gigantic circulation system almost as vital to the life in and around the bay as the blood stream is to a human being. Stop the currents and the bay would turn into a stagnant lagoon; life on its shores would become intolerable.

As the incoming sea water flows into the narrower and shallower areas at the bay's extremities, it tends to pile up. Thus the bay's surface is never level. A boat entering the Golden Gate and sailing south on a maximum flood tide would arrive at the bay's southern end about one hour and fifty-five minutes later and in doing so would sail more than four feet uphill. By that time, however, the tide in the Gate might have begun to ebb, and the actual difference in elevation between the two points could be nearly seven feet.

Each part of the bay is hit by the tide in a particular way, depending on the shape of the bottom and the shoreline; and the tidal effects are felt at surprising distances from the ocean. A flood tide reaching its peak in the Golden Gate exactly at noon will arrive at Alcatraz ten minutes later and wash about an inch higher. It will be another inch or two higher when it hits the Ferry Building at 12:30 and Richmond by 12:40. As the current moves north, the narrowing of the bay between points San Pablo and San Pedro slows it down, and it will not reach Mare Island at the north end until nearly two o'clock. Owing to the pile-up effect, it will rise about six inches higher there than in the Gate.

Only a small proportion of the total current is able to pass through narrow Carquinez Strait; beyond that point the tidal effect begins to decrease gradually. High water will not reach Pittsburg until four o'clock, and there it will fall short by several inches of attaining the high-water level of the Gate. By 6:30 ocean-going ships at the delta port of Stockton, eighty-five miles inland, will be lifted to the high-water mark, and an hour later high tide moving up the Sacramento River will reach the capital city of Sacramento, 108 miles and seven and a half hours from the Golden Gate. Even at these distances the ocean's influence is still strong; there is an average rise and fall of three feet at Stockton and more than two feet at Sacramento.

This does not mean that the same water entering the bay from the ocean travels all the way up the river to California's capital. A high tide in the bay has the effect of raising the mouth of the river, causing it to empty more slowly and creating higher water upstream.

The sea water on the incoming tide may flow seven or eight miles inside the Gate but it does not spread out uniformly in all directions. The greatest part of the flow is confined to two well-defined channels in the bay floor, roughly a mile wide, which extend north and south from the Golden Gate, gradually decreasing in size and branching into smaller tributary channels.

In the shallower water outside the channels, as the distance from the Gate increases, the tidal effect becomes less a flow and more a displacing action; each particle of water moves only a short distance, displacing or nudging the next particle, ultimately causing the pile-up of water at the bay's edges.

Curious current patterns are caused by the delay between the time the tide is high at the Gate and the time it has spread to the farthest corners of the bay. The flood currents may be moving east through the Gate at the same time that the ebb currents are flowing west through Carquinez twenty-five miles away. And when the flow out of Carquinez enters the north end of the bay and first meets the incoming flow from the Gate, the two currents pass each other flowing in opposite directions. Ultimately the flood tide becomes powerful enough to overwhelm the ebb, and the entire water movement is northward.

The sharpest two-directional flow occurs in the Gate itself at a time when the bay currents are still ebbing westward under the center of the bridge and ocean currents are beginning to flood eastward along both shores. When the two currents meet and pass, the result is a tide rip—often marked by a line of foam—and unlucky is the small-boat pilot who gets caught in the middle. The notorious Bonita rip, off the northern head, is sometimes powerful enough to swing a good-sized ship halfway around.

Even though most of the tidal flow is confined to the channels, a tremendous amount of water actually enters and leaves the bay on the tides. On the average one sixth of the bay flows out the Gate on the ebb. This amounts to an average flow through the narrows of the Gate of 2,300,000 cubic feet per second, about three and a half times the volume of the Mississippi River at its mouth.

But so great are the variations of the movements of water in the bay that averages do not begin to convey a true picture of the scope and power of the currents. For example, the average rate of 2,300,000 second-feet is the rate at which the current in the Gate would move if its flow were continuous, like that of the Mississippi. Unlike a river the flow of water in the Gate reverses itself about every six hours. Within that time its rate of flow accelerates from zero at slack water to a maximum at the crest of the tide of 4,600,000 second-feet— about seven times the flow of the Mississippi.

But these figures still apply to an average tide. As a tide

on any particular day exceeds the average, the flow increases proportionally. When the great "flagpole" tide of December 1914 subsided in one enormous ebb, one third of the water in the bay roared out through the Golden Gate in a little over six hours. At the crest of that tide the flow was nearly ten million second-feet—fourteen times the flow of the Mississippi.

Proportionally to its width the Golden Gate probably contains the greatest flow of water in the world.

The Magnetic Moon   The strongest influence on the bay tides, as on the tides of all the oceans of the earth, is the moon. It acts as a magnet in the sky, drawing the waters of the seas upward in a swelling bulge. As the earth rotates daily beneath the moon, the bulge, like the moon, moves completely around the globe once a day. Technically this is a "tidal wave," traveling at a maximum rate of one thousand miles an hour; it is so broad, however, that it does not appear as a wave at all but merely a lifting of the ocean surface.

As the Pacific waters rise along the California coast, they wash high on all the beaches and pour swiftly through the Golden Gate. When the moon is at the zenith over the bay, the current runs high on the rocks of the strait and raises the ships at their wharves along the Embarcadero. Six hours later, when the moon sinks in the west behind the Farallones, the rocks are laid bare and the ships drop visibly lower.

The other daily high tide is caused by a quite different effect of the moon's attraction; in one sense it is not really a high tide at all but an optical illusion.

The earth continues to rotate; about twelve hours after the moon was directly above the bay, it appears on the opposite side of the globe, drawing high tides in the Indian Ocean. It might seem that the result would be a low tide on this side. But the tide here is high again. The explanation, greatly simplified, is this: There are land tides as well as sea tides; the moon exerts a pull not only on the water but on the land mass of the earth as well. From the standpoint of San Francisco, when the moon is on the far side of the earth, its attraction is "down." And its pull on the land hereabouts is greater than its pull on the ocean. As San Francisco itself is pulled down, the waters around it lap higher on its shores, creating a "high tide."

To enjoy the illusion, stand at Fisherman's Wharf and watch the moored boats float higher on the rising bay during this high tide. Actually the bay is staying at relatively the same level, and you and the wharf are being drawn down closer to the water as a result of the moon's gravitational attraction.

The two daily high tides are almost never the same height, and the two daily low tides are also unequal. To designate these differences, seafarers have invented a kind of nautical double-talk. The greater of the two high-water marks is called "higher high water" and the other "lower high water." Similarly, of the two daily low tides which follow, one is known as "lower low water," the other "higher low water."

Oddly enough, the higher of the two daily high tides in the bay occurs not, as might be expected, when the moon is overhead but about twelve hours later when it is on the opposite side of the earth. The explanation for this apparent discrepancy is that, although the moon exerts its greatest pull on this area when it is overhead, the bay takes some time to react to that pull; there is about a twelve-hour delay in the water's response. By that time the moon is on the far side of the earth. Higher high water, therefore, occurs when the moon is almost straight down; lower high water when it is overhead.

The low tides occur, of course, when the moon is near the horizon. Since what goes up must come down, and usually by a compensating amount, in general the higher the bay rises, the lower it sinks six hours later. The highest tides are thus followed by the lowest; higher high water is followed by lower low water.

As the moon makes its twenty-seven-day trip around the earth, its various positions have special effects on the tides. Twice a month it is in line with the sun—at new moon and full moon—and the two spheres pulling together cause the extreme "spring tides." Such a tide has no known causal effect on a young man's fancy; the term comes from the fact that the ocean "springs" above its usual level. When the moon swings closest to the earth—a position described as being "at perigee"—it draws the high "perigean" tides. And when it reaches its greatest distance north or south of the equator and stands near the Tropic of Cancer or the Tropic of Capricorn, it gives rise to the large "tropic" tides.

Usually the spring, perigean, and tropic tides occur at separate times, but on rare occasions they coincide. At such times the moon exerts the greatest pull of which it is capable. The currents charge through the Golden Gate with immense force; the waves leap high against the rocks; the tidal marshes are flooded; and along the waterfronts, gangplanks rise steeply to the decks of high-riding ships.

Winds, Waves, and Quakes   The bay's tides are influenced by other forces, too, far closer than the moon. One such force is the earth's sheath of atmosphere, which itself flows around the globe in tides and currents similar to those of the ocean. One of the great tidal movements of the atmosphere is the motion of air masses from the Pacific onto the North American Continent during a good part of the year. The result is a prevailing breeze from the ocean. Like the ocean currents themselves the prevailing winds are funneled between the converging hills of the Golden Gate and sweep through the narrows with concentrated force.

Such winds are often strong enough to drive the water before them through the strait and create sizable swells. If the tide is at the flood, the wind acts as a "pusher," helping it along, sweeping more water into the bay, and causing it to rise higher than it would otherwise. If the tide is ebbing, its outflow is retarded; the wind, opposing the water currents, scuffs up the foam, blowing the tops off the waves, and the bay's normal blue-green is flecked by countless whitecaps.

The prevailing winds, however, do not always prevail. There are times—especially in the winter—when local disturbances alter the wind currents unpredictably.

Recall that the air acts as a heavy blanket on the earth and its waters, pressing down normally with a weight of nearly fifteen pounds per square inch. If this blanket of air were completely removed from the bay, the surface of the water would rise thirty-four feet. Even a slight decrease in the pressure of the air over the bay—a phenomenon which occurs frequently in unstable weather conditions—can cause the surface to rise measurably. The wind which then rushes into the area to equalize the pressure will tend to pile the water up, adding to the rise.

A notable instance of this odd effect occurred early on the morning of November 21, 1910. Between four and five o'clock the barometric pressure suddenly dropped; as a result the wind, which had been blowing at four miles an hour from the south, increased its velocity to eleven miles an hour. Although the tide was ebbing in the Golden Gate and the water level had been falling, within a period of ten minutes it suddenly rose nearly seven inches.

Since the wind increase was relatively slight, stronger winds and varying pressure are obviously capable of changing the water level a foot or more within a very few minutes, setting up unpredictable shifts in the pattern of currents. Mariners thus sometimes encounter currents exactly the opposite of those to be expected. In extreme cases these wind and pressure changes are strong enough temporarily to reverse the bay's surface currents even at the point of their greatest power—in the Golden Gate.

On September 18, 1869, San Franciscans were alarmed by a rumor that a six-foot "tidal wave" was sweeping across the bay. Some panicky waterfront residents hastened to higher ground to escape the anticipated deluge, but the wave never arrived. Reporters found numbers of people who had "heard tell" of the wave but none who had seen it. Probably it was simply a swell from a passing ship, magnified by someone's imagination. Actually a large tidal wave in a body of water the size of the bay could only be caused by a local earthquake so destructive that the wave would be an unnoticed aftermath.

Tidal waves produced by earthquakes in the far Pacific—more correctly called seismic sea waves—have caused minor damage along the California coast (particularly one which rose to eight and one half feet at some points in 1946), but the bay itself is protected from any such disturbances by the narrowness of its entrance. Earthquakes have had some effects on bay tides, however. Ten minutes after the great San Francisco earthquake of April 18, 1906, which occurred along the San Andreas fault on the ocean floor just off the Golden Gate, the water level in the Gate dropped about four inches. Ironically, much greater disturbances in the bay have been caused by earthquakes occurring several thousand miles away. On November 4, 1952, for example, a quake which centered in the North Pacific off Kamchatka, four thousand miles away, sent the water in the Golden Gate bouncing up and down over a range of three and a half feet. A quake in the Aleutians on March 9, 1957, resulted in a surface oscillation of about two feet, while a sharp jolt in San Francisco two weeks later had little effect on the bay.

The reason for this surprising difference in effect is that the earth shocks were of different types. In the San Francisco quakes the principal movement of the earth was horizontal; the greatest shift was a north-south displacement along the fault. In the Kamchatka and Aleutian quakes, however, there was a large vertical movement of land; the waves, which travel at speeds approaching four hundred miles an hour, were generated by a sudden rise or drop in part of the sea bottom.

Another odd effect on the bay's tides results from the rotation of the earth. The same principle that causes water draining from a bathtub anywhere in the Northern Hemisphere to circle to the right is responsible for a similar tendency in the bay. Although the bay currents do not actually circle, they veer to the right, causing tides higher on one side than on the other, depending on the direction of the current. Thus, high tides may be several inches higher at Richmond than on the opposite shore at San Rafael, at Hunters Point than directly across at Alameda.

Differences in the surface due to all these causes are minuscule compared to the bay's built-in bulge. Like the ocean itself, the bay is not flat but rounded, following the curvature of the earth. So great is the bulge that if it were possible to stand at Petaluma Creek on the north shore and get an unobstructed view to the south, a building in Alviso at the far end, fifty miles away, would not be visible beyond the bulge unless it were at least fifteen hundred feet high—twice the height of the Golden Gate Bridge towers. Further, to an observer on the shore of the bay, any ship is completely hidden by the curve of water at a distance of from fifteen to twenty miles.

The San Francisco River   Nearly one fifth of the bay consists of fresh water, intermingled with the ocean brine. The great outflow of the river has an impact on the bay second only to that of the ocean itself.

Anza and his contemporaries, exploring the bay's shores in the 1770s, followed the estuary east of Carquinez, discovered that the water there was fresh, and carried on long arguments as to whether this was a great river or a fresh-water arm of the bay. Those who believed it was a river called it "El Rio Grande de San Francisco."

A few miles beyond the point to which Anza explored, "the Great San Francisco River" branches into two, the Sacramento from the north—by far the larger—and the San Joaquin from the south. Together they drain California's Central Valley, an area of 60,000 square miles—about the size of all the New England states combined. They join in the delta, a vast natural marsh which has been converted into a prolific farm area laced with channels from the two rivers. Their total annual flow into the bay averages close to 20,000,000 acre-feet, enough to supply water for the city of San Francisco for more than two hundred years. In terms of volume of water this is one of the half-dozen largest river systems in the United States and by far the largest within the boundaries of any single state.

The main source of this tremendous flow of water is another California superlative: the Sierra Nevada. This unbroken granite wall—the longest and highest in the country—extends for four hundred thirty miles down the state's eastern side and is so rugged that for more than half its length it is untraversed by a road of any kind.

High storm clouds drift in from the Pacific, surmount the low ridges of the Coast Range, move eastward across the Central Valley, often trailing long rain banners en route, and hit the peaks of the Sierra, the valley's eastern wall. The mountain barrier forces them to deposit their heavy burden on its western slopes. There much of the condensed moisture is stored in the snow pack or in natural underground reservoirs. The rest flows directly down thousands of creeks and sixteen mountain rivers to the valley floor and the main trunk streams —the Sacramento and San Joaquin. The creeks of the Coast Range flow in from the west. Ultimately, then, most of the water vapor which floats eastward in clouds from the ocean across the coastal hills returns down the river to the bay, the Central Valley's only outlet to the sea.

More than 80 per cent of the natural river runoff from this recurring cycle of clouds, rain, and flow takes place in the first six months of the year. By spring the last of the rains are falling on the Central Valley, the Sierra snows are melting, and the river races full to the bay. Then, as the summer sun beats down out of a cloudless sky, thousands of tributary creeks dry up, streams fall to a trickle, and shrunken tributary rivers meander lazily across the bottoms of channels which just a few months previously had run full, bank to bank.

Not only is there wide variation in the volume of flow from one part of the year to another, however, there are also great variations from year to year. In the dust-dry year of 1924, for example, the flow dropped to a mere 9,000,000 acre-feet. In the flood year of 1907 it rose to 63,000,000. Heavy rains over an extended period are capable of raising the river to formidable heights. Although newly constructed dams, particularly Shasta Dam, on the upper Sacramento, have succeeded in curbing the river's natural floods to some degree, its flow still fluctuates widely. During the great 1955 Christmas floods, which inundated Yuba City and many other areas in the Sacramento Valley, the river rose thirty feet above normal at Sacramento, despite by-passes which carried a great part of the flood waters around the city.

Record Tides   At most seasons, except when the river is very low, its impact on the bay is plainly visible. It is always evident during the rainy season and particularly after heavy floods. At such times a mud-laden tide of river water sweeps down the bay from Carquinez daily, drawing a brown blanket across the blue-green surface. Its advancing front, known to bay mariners as the tidal bore (although technically a bore results only from an ocean tide), is often marked by an audibly churning wave of foam sometimes as much as two feet high, extending for miles across the central bay.

Only the full force of the ocean current, pouring through the Golden Gate at high tide, is able to stem the river and restore the bay's surface for a few hours to its normal color. As soon as the incoming tide begins to slacken somewhat, the bore once more moves down from the north, setting up a simultaneous flow in both directions: the brown surface currents running out and the salt currents a few feet below the surface flowing in. So powerful is this wall of water that some of the captains of the Oakland ferries regularly read the Sacramento newspapers to learn the height of the river upstream and calculate the size of the tidal bore they will have to cope with a day or two later.

On the ebb tide the muddy river waters not only overwhelm the bay but pour out the Golden Gate and color the ocean itself as far as the Farallones, twenty-seven miles offshore.

This tremendous volume of water pouring out of the river in flood season is obviously capable of raising the bay's entire four-hundred-square-mile surface. If a river flood comes at a time when the tides are not very high, its addition to the bay's volume may have little effect. But if it is added to the top of a spring, perigean, or tropic tide, or perhaps even all three combined, it can lift the surface far above its normal high-tide level. Add a strong onshore wind roaring into the Gate, retarding outflow, and the swollen bay will overflow into shoreline areas, flooding marshes, beaches, and low-lying communities.

Such a combination of the elements was responsible for the great tide of December 16, 1914, which lifted the ferryboat flagpoles to the roofs of the sheds. Predicted high water for that date was 6.9 feet in the Gate at 9:47 A.M. By that hour the water was well above 6.9 and still rising. At ten o'clock it stood a full foot above the predicted maximum at the Gate and across the bay in Oakland was several inches higher.

Even that historic tide was exceeded one rainy day in 1940. The tide tables listed a 6.1 high for the day before Christmas that year. But the clouds loosed their torrents, the river ran at flood stage, the wind roared in from the west, and the bay rose and inundated its shores with a tide that stood at 8.2 feet in the Golden Gate—the highest yet recorded. Other parts of the bay ran correspondingly higher. At Alviso the swelling waters rose twelve feet, pouring over levees and sending residents to their rowboats.

Inevitably more water goes out the Gate than comes in. Because the ebb tides are augmented by the fresh-water outflow from the river and other runoff, ebb currents at the Gate are always stronger and swifter than the following flood currents.

Normally twice a month, during the spring tides, when the moon is new or full, the bay surface at low tide drops at least several inches below zero point on the gauges (mean lower low water), resulting in the "minus tides" beloved of clam diggers and abalone hunters. In the ocean the highest spring tides are normally followed immediately by the lowest. But not in the bay. The river floods which raise the bay brimful on a winter high tide also prevent it from sinking as far as it would otherwise on the following low. The lowest recorded tides in the bay have come in dry years when the river outflow was at a minimum. Twice in times of little rain, in De-

cember 1932 and again a year later, the waters of the bay ran
so low that the tidal gauge at the Golden Gate registered
minus 2.5 feet.

Salt and Swimmers   Because the river merges gradually
with the bay above Carquinez, it is not possible to draw a
distinct line where one ends and the other begins. Although
a logical dividing place might be the upper limit of this merging—where the river's fresh water first begins to be slightly
salty—this point continually moves up- and downstream with
the tides and the variations in river runoff.

At the turn of the century the river flowed past Carquinez
in such strength that, when the C. & H. sugar refinery was
first built at Crockett, fresh water was drawn directly from
the strait. But as dams were built upstream and increasing
amounts of water were drawn off for irrigation and domestic
use, the flow decreased. In dry years salt water ran far up
past Carquinez, through Suisun Bay and into the delta,
where it caused trouble for farmers drawing their irrigation
water from the river channels. In the drought year of 1931,
for example, two thirds of the river channels in the delta were
salty. At such times the water rose and fell with the tides as
far upstream on the Sacramento as Verona, the junction
with the Feather River, one hundred thirty miles from the
Golden Gate. In the late summer and fall the amount of river
water flowing into the delta was sometimes barely enough
to balance evaporation, and no fresh water reached the bay
at all.

Since the completion of Shasta Dam in 1945, enough water
has been released from the reservoir during dry months to
prevent the river from falling that low. The more nearly constant flow of the river now acts as a fluid "salt-water barrier,"
exerting sufficient pressure downstream the year around to

keep the bay at bay, so to speak. The point at which the river first hits salt water is now maintained, subject to some seasonal and annual variation, within an area a few miles above Antioch, protecting delta farmlands from salt-water invasion.

Nevertheless the salt content of the bay itself changes widely from year to year, from season to season, and from tide to tide. In general the bay is saltier in dry years than wet ones, in the summer than the winter, and on the flood tide than the ebb.

Outside the Gate the salinity of the ocean is 3.4 per cent, and the waters of the Gate itself average only slightly less —3.1 per cent. At Carquinez, more directly influenced by the river flow, the salinity drops to an average 1.5 per cent, but in the shallow south end of the bay, where there is little fresh-water inflow and high evaporation, the salt content averages close to that of the Gate, making possible commercial salt extraction.

Although the bay's salinity has on occasion proved a menace to delta farmers, it has also been a blessing to dwellers on the bay's shores. Since 1950 most of the shoreline cities have built sewage treatment plants and no longer use the bay as a place to dump their untreated wastes. Nevertheless there is still a considerable amount of industrial waste and some domestic sewage that finds its way into the bay's waters. The circulating currents remove the pollution, however, and the salinity tends to neutralize its effect, since bacteria, which thrive in fresh water, do not reproduce prolifically in salt.

As a result of the treatment plants, in recent years most of the bay has finally been declared officially safe for swimming. There has been no rush of bathers for the beaches, however; water temperatures, even in the warm months of summer and early fall, are low enough to discourage nearly all but the most dedicated members of the swimming clubs.

Although most people who have so much as dipped a toe

in the bay would deny it, the water is considerably above freezing. In fact the average surface temperature at the Golden Gate is identical with the average air temperature in San Francisco—fifty-six degrees. But again, averages are deceiving, and the extremes are wide. Fairly comfortable swimming can be found in the late summer at the extreme northern or southern ends of the bay, where the shallow water is readily heated by the sun and reaches the middle or high sixties. North-end temperatures are kept high in the summer not only by the sun but by the waters of the river, warmed in their journey of hundreds of miles through the heat of the Central Valley. At San Francisco's bay beaches, all near the Golden Gate, swimmers would do well to consult the tide tables; an ebb current from the sun-heated bay will be several degrees warmer than a flood current from the ocean, where the temperature is relatively stable the year around.

In the winter the effect is reversed. The stable temperature of the ocean currents keeps the water near the Gate warmer than the shallow ends of the bay, which cool off rapidly at the end of summer. And the river maintains much of the frigidity it acquired from its origins in Sierra snows. Consequently the coldest part of the bay in January is near Carquinez, where the mercury will register in the low forties—as against a temperature in the middle forties off Palo Alto and a Gate reading of around fifty.

The Bottom   In one sense the river still flows through the valley of the bay much as it did in pre-bay times. When the ocean gradually invaded the valley, it naturally moved first up the channel already carved by the river. As a result the route of the ancient river bed is now the deepest part of the bay; it carries the main currents and is the traffic lane of the big ships. It is joined just inside the Golden Gate by a shallower but similar channel from the south, following the ancient route of Coyote Creek, which flows from the Santa Clara Valley and once drained the southern part of the bay's basin.

The currents, in turn, flow swiftly enough to scour further the ancient channels, maintaining their depth and carving some of them deeper. Consequently, if the bay were drained overnight, the general contours of its basin would resemble roughly those of the former valley. The basin is now much shallower than in pre-bay days, however. Much of the great load of silt, sand, and gravel once carried by the river to the ancient delta beyond the Golden Gate is now dropped in the bay itself. In some areas the original valley floor is covered by more than one hundred feet of river-borne debris.

The process of filling the bay with silt was greatly accelerated during the hydraulic mining period beginning in the 1850s. Up in the Sierra foothills one man with an apparatus like a fire hose and a giant nozzle could cut away a hillside in a few minutes, eliminating the necessity for laborious pick-and-shovel work in the search for gold-bearing quartz. As a result the rivers ran like liquid mud into the bay for many years, and now almost a century later more than a billion cubic yards of Mother Lode sand and silt lie nearly three feet deep in the Suisun and San Pablo areas of the bay.

Although hydraulic mining was belatedly outlawed in 1884, the mountain soil denuded during that period continues to be eroded by rain and streams, intensifying the floods, muddying the rivers and the bay.

These river-borne sediments, plus wastes from ships, cities, and factories, make the bay thickly turbid. Divers who descend into the murky water, investigating wrecks and working on cables, are unable to see ahead of them more than three or four feet. Often a diver can see only a few inches, and most of his work is done by "feel."

By far the greatest part of the bay consists of shallows where the mud has been laid down in thick layers, often so soft that a diver can sink in it over his head without hitting anything solid. At low tide more than three quarters of the bay is less than eighteen feet deep. Off Berkeley, for example, the water is so shallow that in the days of the ferries it was necessary to build a pier three and a half miles out from the shore to reach water deep enough for the boats to dock. For most of its length the Berkeley pier—now frequented only by fishermen—traverses water less than ten feet deep.

At many places off the Bayshore Highway south of San Francisco, a venturesome wader, if he could find a firm bottom, could walk a mile and a half into the bay without getting his chin wet, and at low tide near the San Mateo Bridge he could wade straight out from the east shore five miles and still be only waist deep. But then he would suddenly find himself in trouble, for at that point the bay floor drops off into the central channel. Here the main current has gouged out a canyon about a mile wide and seldom shallower than forty feet, permitting ocean-going ships to dock as far south as Redwood City. The channel continues at lesser depths almost to Alviso. Farther north it broadens to several miles and reaches a depth of one hundred feet beneath the Bay Bridge just west of Yerba Buena Island. In the two main channels, extending north and south from the Gate, the bottom is more firm; here the currents move too swiftly to deposit silt and they lay down a floor of sand and gravel.

At any point in the bay where currents must pass through a narrow passage they are forced to go correspondingly deeper. Although the greatest depth beneath the four-mile-long Richmond-San Rafael Bridge, for example, is forty feet, a short distance to the north where the currents converge in San Pablo Strait they have carved out a bed twice that deep. The greatest depth in Carquinez Strait is ninety-seven feet, and in Raccoon Strait, between Angel Island and Tiburon, where the main channel narrows to a half mile, the power of the rushing water has scoured the bottom to a depth of two hundred feet.

The deepest gorge in the bay's floor has been cut by the prodigious torrents of the Golden Gate. The center of the bridge is suspended over water 318 feet deep. Half a mile west, the currents sweep bedrock at 382 feet below mean low tide, depth enough to swallow a twenty-eight-story building. Farther west, as the currents begin to fan out and lose their power, the bottom grows shallower. A few miles beyond the heads it lies from twenty-four to sixty feet below the surface. Nowhere inside the Farallones does the ocean floor reach the greatest depth of the Gate.

The currents that carved these channels and the primary processes that formed the bay itself are readily visible from its shores. Stand on a hill near the central portion of the bay in springtime and watch the forces that gave birth to the bay re-enact in a day the drama of its creation.

See the river's silty waters roll down from the north in a massive tidal bore and overwhelm the blue currents of the ocean, as if to reclaim this valley for its own. Watch the ocean counterattack through the Golden Gate with a swiftly moving flood that forces back the river and re-establishes the sea's dominion. In this ebb and flow of the conflicting currents that give the bay its shape and substance the act of creation is continually renewed in response to even mightier forces—the flow of countless streams from the perennial fountains of the Sierra, the turning of the earth, the tug of the moon, the rise of the ocean.

To observe the bay's rhythms and understand their meaning, even remotely, is to discern something of immense significance: for dwellers in the cities on its shores the bay is a microcosm of the physical forces at work on this spinning planet.

SUMMER

Even though the sun comes streaming through your window on a bright summer morning, the first thing you hear as you awaken is the bass chorus of foghorns chanting their rhythmic diapason in full voice.

Across San Francisco from the old mansions of Pacific Heights to the crowded apartments of the deep Mission, from the Embarcadero to the slopes of Twin Peaks, the city wakes to the sunshine. But if you have a view to the north, you can look down to the Gate and see the long gray arm of fog several hundred feet high that comes gliding across the water, envelops the bridge, and surrounds Alcatraz in a translucent shroud.

Out in the channel ships bellow their fog warnings and grope blindly, barely moving. Morning commuters from Marin hit the wall of vapor as they leave the protection of the hills and drive out onto the deck of the bridge; they cut their speed, switch on their headlights, then in a few minutes emerge into the sun again as they pass the toll gate and come down the long ramps into the city.

If it's a Saturday or Sunday, the city's parks will be sprinkled with sun bathers, lying on the sloping lawns absorbing the warmth, drowsily listening to the far-off horns. If it's a weekday, office dwellers will gaze wistfully out the windows of downtown buildings, watching the clocks until they can get out for a few minutes of noon sunshine.

Over the water the fog may linger all day. Or it may burn off by noon, and the great voices of the bay will be stilled. But by midafternoon you will begin to hear the bass horns again, and the fog mass will once more move in over the water, spreading to the shores and through the urban valleys, perhaps before dark wrapping the entire city in its thick white summer blanket.

6

"Harbor of Harbors"

THE PARADE OF SHIPS

The explorers and empire builders to whom this boundless bay was a place of destiny—from Crespi to Anza to Dana to Frémont—visualized it pre-eminently as the greatest natural port they had seen: ". . . a harbor of harbors . . ." ". . . the emporium of a new world."

Their visions were prophetic. It was this bay and its water-borne commerce that made San Francisco the capital and first metropolis of the new world on the Pacific. Every ship that sailed into the Golden Gate with men or machinery brought the materials of empire. Every vessel that sailed out with its hold full of California gold or wheat or cattle or oil or cotton added to the power and wealth of the burgeoning West.

In the years following the discovery of gold the economic life of the city was keyed to the arrival of each ship. San

Francisco businessmen anxiously watched the semaphore rigged on top of Telegraph Hill to signal a vessel's appearance in the Golden Gate. So furious was the competition that the more enterprising merchants raced to the ship in longboats to get first choice of its goods and resell them at fantastic prices.

Even now, a century later, the coming of a ship is still an event of major importance. Although twenty vessels may enter the bay in a single day, each arrival sets in motion a chain of activity less frenzied but even more far-reaching than that set off in the old days by the appearance of a full-rigged clipper ship standing into the Golden Gate on the west wind.

Boarding the Pilot   On the highest ridge of Point Lobos, the lookout at the Marine Exchange Station sits watching the ocean, squinting as the glare of the afternoon sun blazes up from the water. At exactly 3:42 he sights a speck on the horizon some twelve miles to the south, just off Point San Pedro. He peers through his telescope, then reports into the telephone connecting him with the Marine Exchange headquarters in the Ferry Building: "*Loch Ryan* at Point San Pedro, 3:42."

There the switchboard operators relay the message to Marine Exchange members. The first call goes to the agents of Britain's Royal Mail Lines—owners of the *Loch Ryan*—in an office on shipping row along lower California Street. Then, in turn, the report goes out across the city and around the bay—to ship chandlers, towboat companies, shipyards, patrol services, Navy headquarters, Quarantine, Customs, Immigration, and Horticultural Service officials: "The *Loch Ryan*, Point San Pedro, 3:42."

Eleven miles west of the Golden Gate Bridge, the two-masted schooner *California*, the wind in her sails, rides the northwest swells, whipped by late afternoon breezes. Inside her main cabin just aft the pilothouse, three middle-aged mariners, puffing on cigars, sit discussing their favorite television shows. All of them are former ship captains and now licensed members of the San Francisco Bar Pilots association.

A member of the crew appears in the door to the pilothouse. "Looks like your ship acomin', Captain," he says.

"It's about time," says the first pilot, rising and walking toward the pilothouse, unconsciously adjusting his gait to the pitching deck. "That's her, all right," he says, peering south through the pilothouse window.

He scans the horizon in other directions. Half a mile west is the lightship, with the big letters "SAN FRANCISCO" painted in white on her bright red hull. Seventeen miles beyond it are the sharp rocky tops of the Farallones. In the opposite direction the outline of the Golden Gate Bridge is barely visible against the coastal hills.

As the *Loch Ryan* draws near, two crewmen lower a small outboard over the side of the *California* and clamber in; they are joined by the pilot, now clad in a trench coat and felt hat. The boat bounces across the waves to the freighter and pulls alongside. The pilot reaches for the ship's rope ladder, waits for the black hull to roll to its lowest point, then catches hold and is carried upward with the return roll. Quickly, before the ship can roll again and dunk him in the racing water, he scrambles up the slippery rungs to the deck.

The *Loch Ryan*, a 498-foot, 10,000-ton merchant vessel, is forty days out of London. In her hold is a miscellaneous cargo of British manufactured goods, including fifteen British Fords, barrels of fertilizer for Central Valley farmers, cartons of processed West Indian nutmeg for San Francisco spice houses, tea from Ceylon, sewing needles, twine, motorcycle parts, window glass, six British jeeps and one hundred cases of dry gin.

On the bridge of the ship the pilot meets the captain, a slender, middle-aged man in the uniform of the British Merchant Marine. The Englishman nods toward the white sails of the *California*, fast diminishing in the distance. "How's the fishing out there?" he asks, smiling.

"Not so good today," the pilot admits. "The salmon aren't hungry. How was your trip up the coast?"

"We had a nasty bit of a head wind. Slowed us down all the way."

The pilot peers toward the Golden Gate. Halfway to shore he spots a double row of eight buoys, marking the channel through the Great Bar.

"Let's put 'er on zero seven zero, Quartermaster," he says.

"Zero seven zero," echoes the helmsman, watching his compass and swinging the ship's wheel to starboard.

Crossing the Bar   As long as men have sailed the seas, the phase of navigation known as crossing the bar has meant the need for special skills and a special alertness to dangers. It has also come to be a universal symbol. Traditionally the bar has meant the dividing line between the perils of the open sea and the security of a good harbor. To Tennyson it was the symbol of the final great boundary, the border between life and death:

> Sunset and evening star,
> And one clear call for me!
> And may there be no moaning of the bar,
> When I put out to sea.

From Bar Harbor on the coast of Maine to Taku Bar on the Yellow Sea many of the ports of the world are known for the size and peril of the submerged bank of land just offshore.

In many ports the bar is a straight line of sand across the entrance, an extension of the beaches built along the coast as the ocean waves eat away at the land, transporting it grain by grain along the shore in the direction of the prevailing currents. In this way the ocean is engaged in a perennial effort to dam off the mouths of bays, rivers, and inlets and is prevented from doing so only by the strength of the tidal currents or river outflow moving through the entrance. Bolinas Lagoon, for example, ten miles north of the Golden Gate, is an inlet which has almost been closed off from the ocean by the long sandspit the currents have built north from Stinson Beach; the power of the tides flowing in and out has been barely sufficient to maintain a narrow entrance channel.

The sand bar off the Golden Gate, an extension of San Francisco's Ocean Beach, would similarly reach across the entrance to the strait and almost completely dam it off if it were not for the power of the tides. But the volume of water flowing out the Gate is so great that it bulges the sandbank out to sea in a submerged semicircle eleven miles long, curving from the vicinity of Fleishhacker Pool three miles south of the Gate to a point five miles offshore and back to the coast just north of Point Bonita.

The Great Bar is a rich composite of materials—mainly sand from coastal beaches but also sediment brought down the Sacramento and San Joaquin rivers, carried out the Gate on the brown ebb tide. Thus beneath the *Loch Ryan* as it crosses the bar may be silty particles from the topsoil of a Sacramento Valley peach orchard or a San Joaquin cotton field, tailings from a Mother Lode gold field panned by a forty-niner, minute flakes of granite gouged from Yosemite Valley by a Pleistocene glacier.

The shallowest water over the bar is at the "Potatopatch," off Point Bonita, so called not because the almost constant whitecaps over it resemble mashed potatoes but because in the old days schooners carrying sacks of potatoes from Bodega Bay sometimes lost their cargoes while crossing it. The bar here is twenty-two feet beneath the surface at mean lower low water. During extreme low tides there is even less clearance, and at such times in the trough between large swells the top of the sandbank may be only a few feet deep. Since a medium-sized freighter draws about twenty feet of water and a large oil tanker will draw more than forty, the bar can be an effective barrier to shipping.

Formerly ships sometimes hit bottom during the crossing, at considerable peril to life and vessel. Now, however, the Main Channel through the bar, at a point just south of center, is maintained by the Army Engineers at a depth of fifty feet, the deepest-dredged ship channel in the world. Even so there is still sufficient danger both here and in the Golden Gate that all foreign vessels and all American vessels from foreign ports are required to take pilots.

Two other channels, one at each end of the bar, are more dangerous and seldom used by large ships. The South Channel skirts the shore in an area where heavy swells can drive a vessel onto the beach. The Bonita Channel, off the northern head, is narrow and full of rocks and reefs.

When the winter swells roll in from the far Pacific and thunder into churning white at the bar, when in the words of the mariners "the bar is breaking," even an experienced navigator often prefers to anchor outside and wait for calmer seas. In the great storms of December 1955 even at the times when a bar crossing was deemed safe, pilots on outgoing ships were sometimes unable to transfer across raging seas to the pilot boat; they were forced to stay on board until the next port of call.

Through the Gate   As the *Loch Ryan* passes between the buoys marking the channel, a Coast Guardsman standing watch inside the immaculately white Point Bonita lighthouse looks up at a calendar on the wall of the lookout room and reads on the line beneath the date: "SUN SETS AT 5:12." Climbing the steel stairway to the light itself, he hoses down the outside glass and pulls back a big dust cover that surrounds the ten-foot-high cylindrical lens.

Downstairs again, he flips a switch turning on the light mechanism; a single five-hundred-watt bulb, magnified by the lenses, flares into a forty-thousand-candlepower beam visible seventeen miles at sea. The Coast Guardsman holds a stop watch on the light to check its timing: two flashes every twenty seconds—a code which identifies the light to mariners.

As the *Loch Ryan* passes between the last of the channel buoys, a ninety-five-foot Coast Guard cutter which has been riding the swells across the strait near the Mile Rock lighthouse approaches the ship.

The freighter slows down, complying with federal law which requires every ship entering the harbor to obtain permission from the Coast Guard to enter. After making identification the Coast Guardsman in charge of the cutter blinks its lights, signaling the ship to proceed.

The *Loch Ryan* is now entering the narrows of the strait where the ocean currents converge, and the streams of rushing water bear the ship along on a strong flood. The quartermaster can feel the force of the current in the tips of his fingers as he grips the wheel. The pilot peers forward from the bridge more attentively and occasionally walks out onto the port or starboard wings, watching all the signs of the current—the powerful eddy inside Point Bonita, the sharp line of a tide rip that appears two hundred yards ahead, the approach of another ship outward under the bridge, the choppy water near the Fort Point shoal. He must calculate the effect of all these forces on his vessel not only at this moment but at various intervals of time in the future. A ship has no brakes; at a normal speed of ten knots it will take fully a mile to stop the *Loch Ryan* even with her propeller in reverse.

In clear, calm weather the pilot's job is difficult enough, but when thick fogs hang through the Gate, he must then guide the ship as if he were blindfolded. Radar is only a supplementary aid and is not always reliable. Even equipped with all the precision instruments of modern navigation, the pilot dares not rely on them alone, and he is ultimately thrown back on the same resources that guided Jason and Ulysses, Columbus and Drake and Ayala—his eyes and ears and his own sixth sense, the intuition of the seasoned mariner.

So he gazes into the fog, perhaps not even able to see the bow of his own ship, and listens for the warning ring of bell buoys marking rocks and shoals, for the whistles of nearby ships, for the sounds of the foghorns along the shore, mentally plotting his own location and course.

If the bow of another vessel should suddenly break through the mists dead ahead, he has only a split second to make his decision. A board of inquiry, meeting after an accident, can take all the time it needs to decide what should have been done. In view of the hazards the rarity of accidents is a tribute to the skill of the men who stand on the bridges of the ships.

But this voyage of the *Loch Ryan* is uncomplicated by wind or fog. Ahead of the ship the twin towers of the Golden Gate Bridge rise in the twilight sky, their red beacons flashing simultaneously. Beneath the center of the bridge, and three miles ahead, the Alcatraz light, swinging in a broad arc, sends out its quick signal every five seconds. As the British freighter passes beneath the bridge, the lights of downtown San Francisco come into view off the starboard bow.

"Better come easy to ninety," the pilot orders. "Zero nine zero."

Chain Reaction   On the end of Meiggs Wharf, the Marine Exchange lookout on duty spots the *Loch Ryan* beneath the bridge. He notifies his assistant, who picks up a mail sack and envelopes containing instructions for the captain and steps outside to the launch moored alongside the wharf. The lookout, meanwhile, phones Marine Exchange headquarters in the Ferry Building, where operators make the same series of calls first made two hours earlier when the *Loch Ryan* was spotted off Point San Pedro. This time the calls trigger more action around the bay.

In the office of the Royal Mail Lines, the dock superintendent phones the pier where the ship is to dock to make sure a crew of line men is on hand to tie it up. Then he leaves for the pier himself. At the end of Pier 25, the call from the Ferry Building is taken by the dispatcher of the Red Stack towboats. He radios the captains of two tugs to meet the ship. Customs, Immigration, and Horticultural Service officials leave their offices on Sansome Street and at Meiggs Wharf to head for the dock and make their inspections. Had the freighter come directly from a foreign country rather than from another coastal port, she would have had to drop anchor in the quarantine anchorage off Treasure Island until Public Health doctors could make a complete inspection.

Off the *Loch Ryan's* starboard bow appear the lights of the two tugs. One of them comes alongside, and its captain, carrying a walkie-talkie, climbs aboard, proceeds to the ship's bridge, and takes over from the pilot, who is now able to relax for the first time since he boarded the ship.

"I think we better make a port landing and dock her stern shoreward," the tug skipper says to the ship's captain.

Now begins the delicate operation of easing ten thousand

tons of ship up to the pier. The tug captain must co-ordinate the pulling and hauling actions of the two tugs, the ship's engines, the ship's rudder, and consider the force of the vessel's momentum and the power of the flooding current. The slightest miscalculation or error in judgment could send the *Loch Ryan's* steel bow plowing into the wharf.

He gives a rapid succession of orders to the tugs through his radio and to the bridge officers of the *Loch Ryan:* "Slow astern . . . half astern . . . hard astarboard . . . drop your starboard anchor . . ."

After forty-eight minutes of tight maneuvering the British freighter stands with her portside along the dock, stern shoreward. The tug captain gives the order to moor the ship. Soon the longshoremen swarm aboard; the hatches are opened; the ship's booms begin to swing above the decks; and the *Loch Ryan's* cargo, from Fords to gin, enters the economic life stream of the region.

More than a dozen times a day, on the average, the activities that accompanied the arrival of the *Loch Ryan* take place, with variations, as the ships of more than one hundred companies sail through the Gate from two hundred seventy world ports. The process of bringing in a ship is changed in detail from time to time, and a shift-over to radio communications is scheduled for the near future, giving the proposed Marine Exchange lookout station on Pier 45 direct voice contact with the pilot boat, tugs, and arriving ships.

The basic significance of ship arrival, however, is undiminished since the days of the semaphore on Telegraph Hill. Economically as well as geographically San Francisco is built on the bay; and the shipping community along lower Market and California streets—including the headquarters of the Big Three Pacific lines—is one of the vital nerve centers of the West.

Captain Matson   Barrel-chested, thirty-two-year-old Captain William Matson may not have known that he was founding one of the great American flag lines when he first sailed out the Golden Gate against the wind in his little schooner *Emma Claudina* in the spring of 1882. But he did know that the course of empire was westward—toward the group of semi-tropical islands just two thousand miles off the Golden Gate. The hold of his vessel carried general cargoes for the growing Hawaiian economy; a few weeks later he brought the *Emma Claudina* back loaded with coconuts, hides, and sugar cane.

Sugar was the "gold" of Hawaii, and it rapidly turned to money in the pocket of the canny Swedish-born skipper. Within five years he replaced the *Emma Claudina* with a brigantine twice as large, the first of three Matson ships to bear the name *Lurline* and ultimately the flagship of a good-sized fleet—Matson's bridge to Hawaii. As trade with the islands boomed, the Matson star rose swiftly. The immigrant seaman became a power in San Francisco business and society and was considered one of the city's best-dressed men, perennially sporting a big carnation in his buttonhole as he dashed down Market Street in the horse-drawn equivalent of a Cadillac. But he remained a hard-driving commander and a persistent innovator, chalking up a number of significant firsts in Pacific shipping: he pioneered in the use of oil instead of coal as ship fuel, installed the first ship's radio, and built the first of the Pacific luxury liners.

The flagship of the present-day Matson fleet is the 18,500-ton luxury liner *Lurline* III, built in 1933. One of the most memorable voyages of the great white ship was in December of 1941. She had left Honolulu for San Francisco with a shipload of vacationers just two days before Pearl Harbor. After the attack she was blacked out and raced desperately for the safety of the Golden Gate, her speed enabling her to outrun enemy submarines, which had sunk several other commercial vessels.

Like other Matson liners she was quickly painted gray and converted to war duty, hauling troops to Pacific outposts. After the war she was refurbished and returned to luxury status. The palatial liner is inevitably one of the sights pointed out to tourists when she is docked at Matson's Pier 35 just below Telegraph Hill.

In 1957 the Matson passenger fleet was quadrupled with the addition of the 14,000-ton *Mariposa* and *Monterey* on the Australia and South Pacific route and the *Lurline*-sized *Matsonia* on the Hawaii run.

The Dollar Empire and the Presidents   Like William Matson, Robert Dollar was an immigrant, but unlike Matson he had a late start in the shipping business. Dollar, born in Scotland, was a lumberman who came to San Rafael on the bay's shore for his health in 1888, made a fortune cutting California redwoods, and entered the shipping business as a side line.

He was crowding sixty when he acquired his first vessel, the *Newsboy*, a diminutive steam schooner, to haul his lumber down from the north to the bay. About that time the Pacific Mail Steamship Company, which had dominated Pacific shipping since the Gold Rush, went into a decline, accelerated by the sinking of its *Rio de Janeiro* in the Golden Gate in 1901. A voyage to the Orient convinced Dollar of the great possibilities of the Far Eastern trade, and the shrewd businessman picked up where Pacific Mail left off, sending his vessels to Japan and China.

A measure of his business acumen was his curious two-way trade in railroad ties. In his mills in the Northwest he cut ties from the fir forests and carried them on his ships to Tientsin for Chinese railroads. Then the ships proceeded to Japan, where they picked up ties made of oak and hauled them back to San Francisco for the Southern Pacific's lines.

The fleet of vessels with the dollar sign on their funnels expanded until it was the largest line flying the American flag. Lumberman Dollar became known as "Captain" Dollar, although he had never skippered a ship. The old man was tall and lanky, cultivating a white goatee that gave him a striking resemblance to Uncle Sam—a fact that may have been an asset in dealing with Congressmen for legislative favors.

His main interest had long since shifted from lumber to shipping, but the methodical Scot retained two habits developed in his lumbering days: He read his Bible regularly, and he kept a meticulous diary, in which he stored up odd scraps of information and business ideas much as some people save apparently useless pieces of string.

The diary, at least, paid off well. Bit by bit, as he traveled the world on his own ships, he acquired enough lore on international business conditions to enable him to begin his greatest business venture at a time of life when most men are ready for the grave—or in it. In 1924, at the age of eighty, he launched a new fleet of passenger liners—each named for a U.S. president—on an unprecedented round-the-world service, sailing out the Golden Gate to the Orient and returning via Europe and Panama.

In the depression year of 1931, at eighty-seven, he further astounded the business community by launching two new super-luxury liners for the transpacific trade, the *President Coolidge* and the *President Hoover*.

Dollar died in 1932, forty-four years after bad health had brought him to the bay to spend his presumably declining years. After his death the shipping empire he had built began to run into shoal waters. Among other mishaps the *President Hoover* was stranded and lost on a beach in Formosa. Unable

to repay government loans, the line was taken over by the
U. S. Maritime Commission in 1938, renamed the American
President Lines, and operated by the commission for four-
teen years.

After World War II A.P.L. once again resumed the round-
the-world service inaugurated by Dollar. Back in private
hands under the presidency of San Franciscan George Killion, A.P.L. ships served seventy thousand sea miles around
the globe, making it one of the longest steamship lines on
earth.

The flagship of the fleet is the 23,500-ton *President Cleveland,* which alternates with her sister ship, the *President
Wilson,* and the *President Hoover* in sailing through the
Golden Gate twice a month on the transpacific route. Killion
also plans to double A.P.L.'s round-the-world schedules and
build for the transpacific run a new super-liner which will be
one of the half-dozen largest passenger vessels afloat.

The Golden Bear   The heritage of Robert Dollar does not
rest with A.P.L. alone. A dynamic, hard-bitten former pro-
tégé of Captain Dollar, Thomas E. Cuffe, heads the newly
formed Pacific Far East Line and operates it in the best
Dollar tradition. P.F.E.L. was founded just after World War
II, under Cuffe made the most of the expanding opportunities
in the Far Eastern trade, pioneered in new methods of carrying refrigerated cargoes, and as a result rose rapidly to become the fast-growing youngster of the bay's Big Three. The
California Golden Bear on the funnels of its freighters, many
of which are named for bears (*Japan Bear, Korean Bear,*
etc.), has become one of the bay's best-known trademarks.

Further evidence that Cuffe inherits much of old Dollar's
toughness, shrewdness, and aggressiveness can be found in
his recent daring venture in requesting government permis-

sion to add Hawaii to P.F.E.L.'s ports of call, an attempt to compete with giant Matson in the island trade.

Ranking behind the bay's Big Three in numbers of locally owned ships is the tanker fleet of Standard Oil of California, operating from the company's long wharf at Point Richmond. In addition to its more than two dozen tankers, Standard charters a number of super-tankers—vessels so big they cannot tie up at the wharf when fully loaded but must first discharge most of their liquid cargo to normal-sized tankers while anchored in deep water off Treasure Island.

The largest liners to call regularly in the bay are the four buff-colored ships of Britain's Orient Line—the *Orsova, Oronsay, Orion,* and *Orcades,* up to 29,000 tons, calling here on their westbound round-the-world schedules.

The Stream of Cargoes   About 40 per cent of all the freighters sailing through the Gate fly the flags of other nations. Consistently leading the parade of foreign vessels are the ships of the seafaring Norwegians, who operate many vessels which ply between the United States and Asia and seldom go to their own country at all.

Second in numbers to the ships of Norway are the low-slung, streamlined vessels of Japan, most of them built since World War II; they bring fish, wood products (continuing Captain Dollar's trade in railroad ties), wool and cotton cloth, china and tea, and sail away with millions of dollars' worth of rice from the Sacramento Valley and cotton from the San Joaquin, great quantities of gas and oil from bay area refineries, hundreds of thousands of tons of California barley and rye, dairy products for Japanese consumers, iron ore, scrap iron, and machinery of all kinds for Japan's booming industries.

Close behind in third place are the ships of Great Britain,

carrying side by side in their holds commodities that are traditionally supposed to be kept as far apart as possible; their most valuable cargoes are liquor (scotch, gin, ale) and automobiles (Austins, Hillmans, Morrises, MGs, Jaguars, British Fords, and an occasional Rolls-Royce). Swedish and Danish vessels are next in number of arrivals in the bay, followed by those of the Netherlands and France.

Although Japan is second place in terms of numbers of foreign ships in the bay, that country is by far the bay area's best single customer. Ships of all nations sailing out the Golden Gate carry more than twice as much tonnage to the Japanese archipelago as to second-place Canada. Hawaii is a close third, followed by the Philippines. Next come Atlantic areas—Puerto Rico, the Low Countries, Britain, and West Germany. On the mainland of Asia, India ranks first.

By far the greatest tonnage going out the Gate—about one third of the total—is in petroleum products from bayside refineries. Most of it is carried in tankers which load directly from the wharves of the major oil companies along Contra Costa County's oil coast—Standard at Richmond, Union at Oleum, Tidewater-Associated at Avon, and Shell at Martinez.

On outgoing freighters, as distinguished from tankers, the heaviest cargoes are fruit from California orchards (principally canned and dried), barley and rye from the state's rolling foothills, bales of cotton from the San Joaquin, rice from the banks of the Sacramento, iron ore from Utah, scrap iron from many parts of the country, lumber from the northern forests, vegetables (canned, dried, and frozen) from California truck farms, and salt produced from the bay itself. In terms of dollars, however, all these cargoes are outvalued by machinery, destined for the rapidly industrializing nations around the far shores of the Pacific, where it is installed in new factories from Yokohama to Hong Kong to Bombay.

Ships inbound through the Golden Gate bring crude oil for bay refineries in such great quantities that it exceeds in tonnage all other imported cargoes combined. Much of it comes from the oil fields of the southern San Joaquin via pipe lines to the coast above Santa Barbara. But even all the rivers of petroleum from the oil wells of California cannot satiate the thirsty refineries; millions of tons are shipped from across the Pacific, principally from the islands of Indonesia, source of 75 per cent of the imported crude; most of the rest is from beneath the sands of oil-rich countries around the Persian Gulf.

From the cane fields of the Hawaiian Islands come shiploads of raw cane sugar, the second-biggest incoming cargo. It is unloaded at the big C. & H. refinery at Crockett, on Carquinez Strait. After refining much of it is distributed to bay area points on special white ferry-like sugar boats. Also from the islands come great quantities of canned pineapple.

Canadian lumber companies send massive rolls of newsprint for Northern California publishers. The Philippines are the source of another bulky cargo coming in the Gate: copra, the dried and broken kernel of the coconut, is unloaded at special docks at Pier 84 in San Francisco, as anyone with a sensitive nose who drives down Third Street is well aware. It reaches the consumer principally in the form of soap and cooking oils.

Another aromatic cargo—coffee—is close to copra in weight but ranks first by far in value of all imports into the bay; it is worth four times as much as all the crude oil brought in. The area around the San Francisco end of the Bay Bridge is often fragrant with the smell of roasting coffee, most of it shipped from Colombia and Brazil to the plants of the half-dozen major companies near the Embarcadero. One of every twelve cups of coffee consumed anywhere in the world is made from green coffee beans shipped in through the Golden Gate.

From Peru come vessels heavy with lead ore for industrial use; from Mexico, gypsum for fertilizers; from Costa Rica and Panama enough bananas to make a million banana splits every day.

Pacific Era   In more than one sense is this bay, as Padre Font wrote in 1776, "a harbor of harbors." Within this one great harbor—the bay and its tributaries—are more than two dozen separate harbors of all kinds and sizes from the waterfront of San Francisco itself to the barge docks at Sacramento, 108 miles from the Golden Gate.

One of the most important is the Navy dock in Oakland at the largest naval supply installation in the United States. Both commercial and naval ships haul supplies from here to Navy bases all over the Pacific. From Fort Mason in San Francisco sail the big gray steamers of the Military Sea Transport Service, carrying servicemen and their families to Pacific outposts. Including also the shipyards at Hunters Point and Mare Island, the training and receiving center at Treasure Island, and several other major installations, the San Francisco Naval Base is the nation's largest, and the Navy is the bay area's biggest employer. The Army, too, is represented in the bay shipping scene by the Oakland Army Terminal.

Of the bay's five general-cargo ports the two giants of San Francisco and Oakland-Alameda run about neck-and-neck in tonnage, leading by a substantial margin the three newer ports of Stockton, Redwood City, and Richmond. Stockton, eighty-five miles from the Golden Gate up the dredged channel of the San Joaquin River, specializes in Central Valley products. A similar channel is planned for the Sacramento River and will make California's capital the sixth major bay area port. Redwood City, twenty miles south of San Francisco, ships large tonnages of Leslie Salt and Henry Kaiser's Permanente Cement, both of which are produced nearby.

Richmond is a special case. Besides its privately owned general cargo wharves its city limits also include the long wharf of Standard Oil at its Richmond refinery. And when Richmondites add Standard's great oil tonnage to that of their general-cargo docks, they are able to claim that Richmond handles more than twice the tonnage of San Francisco and Oakland combined. Although the two big harbors are also outranked in tonnage by Contra Costa's other oil ports, in terms of dollar value of cargoes they are still in the lead.

The bay's abundance of separate ports is an advantage in some respects but a handicap in others. The handicap is man-made, however, and can be eliminated. The imperative need of bay shipping is for a single port commission or authority to put an end to sectionalism and co-ordinate the efforts of all ports to take advantage of the bay's vast trade potential.

That potential is often overlooked because of misleading statistics. For the bay as a whole tonnages in recent years have remained the same or gradually increased. But this apparent stability is deceptive; it conceals a development of inestimable importance for the future of the bay as a center of commerce. The entire shipping picture is being revolutionized as the pattern of water-borne trade undergoes a major historical change.

Before World War II two thirds of the ships which sailed into the Golden Gate had come through the Panama Canal from Eastern ports. But owing to the increasing movement of goods by rail and truck, this intercoastal trade is now less than one sixth of the total. Similarly, of the two hundred ships that once carried general cargoes up and down the Pacific coast scarcely a dozen remain. World War II accelerated the trend to rail and truck transport. The government commandeered all the ships for war purposes; nearly all domestic cargoes were forced to move by rail and truck and continued to do so after the war was over.

But this drastic decline in the coastwise and intercoastal commerce has been counterbalanced, in the postwar years, by the general increase in foreign trade. Ships which once carried holds full of Northern California products to other coastal ports and to the East are now going overseas. Los Angeles, Philadelphia, and New York are being replaced as customers by Yokohama, Manila, and Hong Kong. The passenger trade is booming correspondingly. In 1955 there were three passenger liners calling San Francisco home port. Two years later there were eight, with plans afoot for more to be added as quickly as they could be built.

This is the beginning of a trend which promises to continue indefinitely if the bay area shipping community can resolve intramural rivalries and grasp the opportunity. For the current expansion of the Pacific trade is a sign of the most significant fact of the mid-twentieth century: the awakening of Asia. The industrial revolution is coming to Asia's ancient lands with explosive speed and impact. Latin America, too, is beginning to feel the stirrings of basic change.

With the growing hum of new factories in all the nations around the shores of the Pacific increasing numbers of ships can sail out the Gate with tools and machinery to supply the new industries; with food and clothing and consumer goods to be sold to the new wage-earners; with agricultural and technical experts to help increase production; with artists, educators, and scientists to facilitate cultural interchange; with tourists to see for themselves the opening of a new historical era.

All this as yet is only a prospect; the present increase in foreign trade is but a beginning, yet it is evidence of an immeasurable opportunity. Once again, as in the past, this bay seems a symbol and promise of mighty events to come.

SUNDAY SAILORS AND GUARDIAN ANGELS

No one knows the bay more intimately than the amateur sailors who cruise its surface on weekends in their own boats, sailing before the wind or plowing a wake in power craft, competing in regattas, exploring the shores and islands, or riding the waves and currents on leisurely cruises to nowhere.

To the boatmen the bay means complete release from workday routine; it offers the recreation and renewal that come from firsthand contact with the elements—with the sun and fog and rising tides, with the roaring winds and flowing waters.

Sun and Scud   They sail the bay in craft of all sizes, from sputtering outboards to huge Diesel power cruisers, from one-man sailboats to long rakish yachts which can cruise to Hawaii or the South Seas. Veteran bay yachtsmen, even those who have navigated in such harbors as Hong Kong and Rio de Janeiro, claim that no place in the world is it possible to sail amid more spectacular surroundings and nowhere can be found such a variety of boating conditions at any one time.

At the same moment on the same day children learn to sail on the pondlike surface of Belvedere Lagoon or Berkeley's inner harbor; water skiers caper off Tiburon's Paradise Cove; sails hang limp in the lee of Angel Island while passengers sun-bathe on the decks; and out in the channel off Alcatraz stiff winds from the Gate send the largest boats scudding across the whitecapped waves and churning currents, spray flying high and masts tilting at a dizzy angle under conditions testing the skill of the most rugged yachtsmen.

Although boating on the bay is a year-round sport, the official summer season begins on the first Sunday in May with the traditional opening-day procession. Hundreds of craft of every description head for the rendezvous under the Golden Gate Bridge at noon, flags flying, balloons blowing, and firecrackers popping. Then, led by the pilot boat *California*, they parade back past the Marina in droves so thick the water is scarcely visible, their passengers shouting good-natured insults from boat to boat. After the procession most vessels head for sheltered coves in the lee of Angel Island or the Tiburon Peninsula; many finish off the day—and nearly every day of the season—tying up for refreshments and post-mortems at the mecca of bay boatmen, Sam's Cafe in Tiburon.

The bay's passage to the interior at Carquinez enables a boat to sail through the coastal mountains into the delta, an explorer's paradise, with a thousand miles of winding channels among a maze of islands. Often during summer vacations larger boats explore the delta's fresh waters and tie up together on riverbanks or in lagoons for a week or two while their passengers sun-bathe, swim in the delta's fresh waters, and hold outdoor barbecues in the warm evenings of the Central Valley.

The spectacular rise in the popularity of small boating has left the owners of the big yachts a tiny minority. It has brought to the bay thousands of outboards and small sailboats operated by people who would never have dreamed of owning a yacht but who nevertheless find relaxation, sport, and beauty on the broad surface of the bay.

They find conviviality there, too. Bay boatmen are no exception to the general rule that, wherever there are two or three Americans gathered together, they will form an organization. There are twenty-five yacht harbors in the bay, fifteen yacht clubs, and separate organizations for each of more than thirty classes of boats, each sponsoring innumerable social affairs, cruises, and regattas.

So varied and changeable are sailing conditions that even experienced boatmen occasionally underestimate the bay, to their inevitable embarrassment. One organizational race of small sailboats from Sausalito to San Francisco turned into a debacle when the breeze whipping through the Gate proved too much for them. Only a few of the tiny craft finished the course. The rest flipped over; their passengers were fished out of the bay by rescue craft, shivering but unhurt.

The Big Swim   Swimmers as well as boatmen find the bay unpredictable. Climaxing the year for the rugged aquatic enthusiasts who brave the bay's chill waters are the annual Golden Gate swims sponsored by Aquatic Park swimming clubs. Carefully picking a time when the tide is slack in early morning to avoid currents and winds, the swimmers dive in near Fort Point and head for Lime Point, a mile away.

Yet the most painstaking precautions cannot prevent the bay from acting up. Although the winners usually plow across the channel in a little over twenty minutes, slower paddlers can expect to be caught by the rising tide and often have to finish the race in a rowboat. One year two strong swimmers were well ahead of the field and sprinting for the finish when they hit an adverse current and were held to a standstill, arms flailing; the man far behind in third place was caught in an opposite current and went churning past the other two to win the race.

In the 1928 contest nearly two hundred swimmers dove off in bright sunshine but were suddenly enveloped by a thick fog which seemed to come out of nowhere. They quickly lost sight of land, their boats, and each other. Less than one hundred ever located the far shore. Before the bewildered amphibians were finally all rounded up and fished out, they had been scattered all the way from the Gate to Alcatraz.

The two most **bizarre** swims across the Gate were both marked by favorable conditions. In 1928, as the result of an argument between the late horse-race impresario Bill Kyne and restaurateur "Shorty" Roberts of Roberts-at-the-Beach, Kyne bet Roberts $1000 that a horse could not swim the Golden Gate. Shorty took the bet, gave swimming lessons to a twelve-year-old harness horse named Blackie, and piloted the animal successfully across the Gate in twenty-three minutes by hanging to his tail.

In 1955 a San Francisco muscle man named Jack La Lanne strapped a tank of air to his back and, accompanied by a boat, made the crossing under water, frogman style.

Both Blackie and the frogman were lucky. A quick change in the currents or a sudden fog could have put a swift end to either attempt. Swimmers and boatmen alike can testify that even when the bay is deceptively calm its changeability is an unpredictable hazard. For the hardy this is a welcome challenge; but there is no doubt that it can also be a menace. Not only do sudden winds sometimes overturn small boats; high waves swamp them; outgoing tides leave them stranded on sand bars; swift currents can wash them far from shore or prevent their return; fogs can leave them groping blindly. The infrequency of serious accidents is due in large measure to the alertness of the unsung heroes of the bay—the men of the United States Coast Guard.

Rescues and Bridge Jumpers　　The Coast Guardsmen are the traffic cops, ambulance corps, rescue teams, supervisors, general nursemaids, and guardian angels of the bay's mariners, both amateur and professional.

The nerve center of the Coast Guard's Twelfth District, which includes the Northern California coast, is in a large room high in San Francisco's Appraisers Building, with big switchboards and control panels where specialists keep tab on every major vessel in the area and direct rescue operations by radio and phone. Boats, planes, and helicopters are ready to go into action from five bay rescue stations; their crews are kept busy at a variety of tasks from taking stranded fishermen off rocks at high tide and finding duck hunters lost in the fog to recovering suicides from under the Golden Gate Bridge and saving the passengers and crew in such a major disaster as the sinking of the *Benevolence* in 1950.

Occasionally Coast Guardsmen have to fish out jet pilots who have bailed out or flipped into the water near the Alameda Naval Air Station and at least once were called on to rescue a cow who had wiggled loose from a sling as she was being loaded on a ship, bowled over two longshoremen and took a header over the side into the bay. A Coast Guardsman who was handy with a rope lassoed the swimming bovine and towed her to safety.

Sometimes rescue operations are hampered by spectators. On one occasion a Coast Guard patrol boat was sent out to check up on a young boy whose homemade raft had become stranded in the mud off Alameda as he paddled around with two companions, a dog and a cat. The crew found the boy and his passengers inaccessible from the boat but in good spirits and willing to wait until a rising tide would take him off the mud. The only real trouble came from a portly newspaper photographer who had waded out for a shot of the stranded trio, sank to his waist and floundered helplessly in the ooze, forcing the Coast Guard to summon a helicopter to extricate him.

Usually the patrolmen are faced with jobs of a more serious and hazardous nature. One day in 1950 a workman at the Union Oil refinery at Oleum turned the wrong valve and a quarter million gallons of gasoline escaped out across the surface of the bay, covering a three-acre area. Any spark or match flame on a boat floating through it could have turned the entire surface into a sheet of flame. Hastily summoned Coast Guard patrols rode herd on the inflammable mass and warned passing vessels away as it drifted with the ebb tide toward San Francisco and returned north toward Mare Island on the flood, finally breaking up after a nervous twelve hours. The only casualties, the Coast Guard reported, were large numbers of sick fish.

The most grisly of the Coast Guard jobs is assignment to the boat crew at the Fort Point station. This crew recovers suicides, who plummet from the deck of the Golden Gate Bridge at the rate of eight a year. Quick action by the patrol results in a recovery of some 70 per cent of the bodies. Although this job is not among the Coast Guard's official duties, it performs the service as a matter of policy.

A jumper hits the water traveling eighty miles an hour; the impact is so great as to mean almost certain death. But a twenty-two-year-old girl named Cornelia Van Ierland, who claimed she never intended to jump, beat the odds. She took a walk on the bridge one day in 1941 and made the mistake of looking over the rail. The dizzy height held an almost fatal fascination.

"I don't know what happened," she said later. "I had an irresistible impulse to jump, and suddenly I clambered over the railing and fell into space. I couldn't help it. I don't know what made me do it. I had no sensation of falling . . . I was conscious every moment."

Her screams were heard by painters on the bridge and the sailors on a passing destroyer. A Coast Guard boat picked her out of the water, fully conscious, seven minutes after she had gone over. The impact had torn her shoes off, shredded her clothing, broken both arms, and fractured a vertebrae. Doctors marveled at her survival and recovery—the only person known to have lived after an unbroken fall from such a height.

In 1947 a stunt man named Fred Cushing was found drifting under the bridge in a rubber life raft and claimed he had just done a Steve Brodie, but he had no witnesses and could find no one to believe him. A year later another acrobat named "Dusty" Rhodes actually made the attempt. He strapped himself into a tight suit and a helmet, took a deep breath, and went over the rail. He was killed on impact.

In Brodie's leap off the Brooklyn Bridge he had fallen only 135 feet, about half the height of the deck of the Golden Gate Bridge. A stunt man named Bob Niles finally succeeded in surviving the jump by using the only piece of equipment that could possibly do any good—a parachute.

All suggestions for diminishing or preventing bridge suicides—including fences, nets, twenty-four-hour patrols, and even a psychiatrist's office at the bridge entrance offering free consultations—have been dismissed as impractical.

The Keepers of the Seabound Lights   From the lightship outside the bar to the guide lights in the Stockton Channel the Coast Guard maintains about four hundred "aids to navigation"—lighthouses, foghorns, and buoys with lights, bells, or whistles—to keep mariners from going aground or colliding in bad weather.

Since the Coast Guard took over all U.S. light stations from the old Lighthouse Service in 1939, the pattern of life in the lighthouses has changed. Gone is the traditional old keeper who climbed the circular stairs each evening to turn on the light, perhaps living out his lonely life on his isolated post—unless, like the legendary keeper of the Eddystone Light, he occasionally frolicked with a mermaid. He has been replaced by trained crews of uniformed young men who serve an appointed term of about one year at a station then depart for other duty. They do their frolicking not with mermaids but whatever company they may find on their regular "shore leaves."

And "shore leave" is no misnomer for the seventeen Coast Guardsmen who man the lightship *San Francisco,* anchored ten miles at sea, and who stay aboard three weeks at a stretch before going ashore for a week-long holiday. The *San Francisco* is the initial target of all mariners heading for the bay. At night she flashes a 13,000-candlepower light, and in fogs her horn sends its bass warning into the gloom.

Since 1898 this 128-foot vessel and its predecessors have anchored at this spot to guide ships to the Golden Gate. History was made aboard the decks of the lightship shortly after it first dropped its hook outside the bar. On August 23, 1899, it originated what is believed to be the first long-distance radio message ever transmitted in the United States. The story is told by Hans Christian Adamson in his *Keepers of the Lights.* At the Cliff House, ten miles away from the lightship, anxious monitors that day picked up the faint buzz of the ship's wireless, spelling out in code the historic words: "Sherman is sighted." The elated listeners quickly phoned the message to the newspapers. It signified the approach of the troop transport *General Sherman,* bringing home a shipload of victorious soldiers from the Philippines after the Spanish-American War.

When the Coast Guard took over the lighthouses, it was provided that the civilian keepers would be able to remain at their stations until retirement. One keeper retired in 1948 after setting an extraordinary record of twenty-two years on a station even lonelier than the lightship—the Mile Rock light, a single tower which seems to grow out of one of a pair of tiny rock islets off Land's End a mile south of the main ship channel.

After the disastrous wreck of the *Rio de Janeiro* off Fort Point in 1901, a clamor arose for a more adequate marking of the channel through the Gate. As a result the Mile Rock tower was constructed in 1906, under great difficulty, from an anchored barge which often rolled and pitched in the violently heavy swells, frequently forcing the crew to suspend work.

Mile Rock has the reputation of being one of the toughest posts in the Coast Guard—psychologically if not physically. The four Coast Guardsmen who now man the rock stay on duty in its cramped quarters for three weeks at a time and, like the lightship crew, are off every fourth week in rotation. The only means of access is a Coast Guard boat which calls once a week with supplies, mail, and a week's newspapers. The man who is to board stands on the bow of the boat as it rises and falls on the swells and reaches for a rope ladder dangling from a boom high above. He climbs the forty-foot ladder, then hauls up a week's supply of provisions on a rope, justifying the saying among Coast Guardsmen that "On Mile Rock they raise all their own food."

In recent years life on the rock has become more tolerable due to the installation of a television set for morale purposes. Although the light itself is seventy-eight feet above the water, the windows around it are sometimes wet with spray, and in winter powerful storm waves batter not only the rock base but the tower itself, shaking the structure from top to bottom with the force of a respectable-sized earthquake.

At such times boat landings are impossible, and there is no escape from the rock until the seas calm down. Crew members admit there are sometimes some anxious moments when the building shudders and shakes, but they become philosophical after a few such experiences.

"You keep telling yourself," says one of them, "that this place has been here for fifty years and has stood everything the ocean could throw at it, and it'll probably be here a long time yet."

The building will probably be there, in fact, longer than there are people to man it. It is planned to make Mile Rock a station that can be operated from the shore by remote control. Automation is very complicated and expensive, however. A special $40,000 cable would run across the floor of the Gate from the Fort Point station. But the light is not visible from that station; the lookout at Point Bonita across the Gate would telephone Fort Point when the visibility decreased to the point where it was necessary to turn on the foghorn or light.

The Lights along the Shore   The Point Bonita lighthouse, along with Mile Rock, is the guardian of the outer Gate. A light was first set up on the highest peak of the promontory in 1855 to guide the gold seekers, but twenty-two years later it had to be moved to the extreme tip of the point two hundred feet lower to escape the strata of fog that often enveloped the peak. The building erected in 1877 still stands, housing the original lens, imported from France.

Among Point Bonita's traditions, as related by James A. Gibbs, Jr., in *Sentinels of the North Pacific*, is the story of a keeper who was on duty one stormy night in January of 1915 when the steamer *Eureka* piled up on the rocks below. He spotted its flares, raced down the trail to the top of the cliff with a rope and lowered himself over the precipice. Literally reaching the end of his rope, he made the agonizing discovery that he was still a considerable distance from the bottom and had to pull himself back up, hand over hand, lashed by wind, rain, and spray. He then ran several miles to obtain a rescue party, which succeeded in saving all but one of the wrecked ship's crew.

Although the Point Bonita lighthouse is on the mainland and seems far more secure than the isolated Mile Rock station, it actually is on rapidly eroding ground, and there is a question as to how many more years it can continue to be operated with safety. The headland on which it stands is separated from the peninsula by a connecting ridge of crumbling rock which is further eroded by landslides every winter. A trestle which spanned the worst area was undermined several years ago and had to be replaced by a suspension bridge. In the great Christmas storms of 1955 a huge slide completely obliterated the trail above the bridge, and the crew had to scramble across sliding rocks. The point is completely unprotected and takes the full fury of storm waves which often roll in from the ocean with sufficient impact to shake the entire headland.

The lights of the inner bay, protected by the sheltering arms of the Golden Gate, face no such problems. The Point Diablo light, midway on the north shore of the Gate between Bonita and the bridge, is operated by remote control from the Lime Point lighthouse, now dwarfed by the north tower of the bridge directly above it.

The oldest lighthouse on the Pacific coast is at Alcatraz. The island, at mid-channel in the direct path of ships entering the Gate where the fogs are thickest, was an obvious menace to shiploads of arriving Argonauts, but evidently no one was able to take time out from fortune-seeking to attend to safety measures until six years after the discovery of gold.

The lighthouse constructed in 1854 lasted until 1909, when it was about to be obscured by the high walls of the Army prison being erected there. A forty-foot tower was built and still stands, high above the prison buildings, resembling the traditional lighthouse more than any of the bay's other lights. The light itself is also traditional, not the off-and-on type like most others in the bay area but the old-style revolving kind which sweeps the sky, sending its beams in a great circle out through the Golden Gate, over the roof tops of San Francisco, across the East Bay cities then the hills of Marin, visible as a quick flash every five seconds. Its 100,000-candlepower light is visible in clear weather for twenty-one miles and is the brightest navigation light in the bay.

Among the bay's half-dozen other light stations the most picturesque is the Southampton Shoal light, which resembles a San Francisco mansion of the pre-earthquake vintage somehow transported to the middle of the bay between Angel Island and Richmond. It is a spacious white frame structure with broad porches and a high Victorian cupola from which its light beams. It rests on a submerged "island" seven feet deep at this point and two miles long. Ships bound for Richmond are forced to detour around the shoal to the north and double back in a sharp turn.

The Voices of the Bay   To many a visitor to San Francisco the foghorn chorus which often rises from the bay and pervades most of the city is simply a mournful din of moans and wails forbidding slumber. To the unaccustomed ear the sound of the horns is eerie and doleful—as it evidently was to science-fiction writer Ray Bradbury. In one of his short stories a dinosaur-like monster of the deep rises from the sea to embrace a fogbound lighthouse in response to what he believes is the mating call of his kind.

To old residents, however, the horn chorus is a particular kind of music; its solemn rhythms weave a haunting pattern of sound identified with home and night and the fogged-in bay. Because they seem loudest after midnight, when the city is still and are often heard through the curtain of slumber, these voices of the deep seem somehow connected with the dark regions of the subconscious and the pleasant half-death of sleep.

Those who maintain that the horn chorus is a special kind of music are backed by expert opinion. In 1954 music professor William S. Hart (who has never slung a six-gun) composed a foghorn concerto based on a tape recording of the horns sounding with their normal rhythms.

"The burden of the music," wrote critic Alfred Frankenstein in the San Francisco *Chronicle*, "is carried by the piano, which dances along in splashy, melodious style, playing around the fog horn notes, incorporating them into its own musical fabric . . ."

To mariners guiding their vessels into the bay the horns are a different kind of music; they are welcome signs of home and of safe harbor close by. They are warning, too, of lurking dangers, of reefs and rocks and shoals; and the imaginative sailor may hear in their bellows the moaning of the drowned passengers of ships which have sunk in these waters. But basically the horns are guides, and the pilot with ears attuned to their individual tones and rhythms can plot his position with accuracy though he be blinded by fog.

To Coast Guardsmen in lighthouses the horns are primarily a duty, to be attended with the same vigilance required by the maintenance of the lights themselves. Day or night, when the fog approaches to within five miles seaward or three miles within the bay, the horns are turned on, though the lighthouse itself may be in sunshine or bright moonlight.

The rhythm and tone of each horn is a product of careful research by Coast Guard planners to compose the medley which will be heard to best advantage by fog-blinded mariners. The most obvious danger is that the horns would blast simultaneously and merge into a single sound which would prevent the pilot from distinguishing the tone and position of each. So horns in the same area must be of different types, sounded at different intervals on different pitches.

In order to obtain a variety of sound the great voices are

produced by three different kinds of instruments—the air diaphragm, the diaphone, and the siren. In each case all the noise is produced by a surprisingly small instrument. The diaphragm is a simple disk up to a foot in diameter with an attached cone-shaped horn or resonator about thirty inches long. When vibrated by an air motor or by electricity it emits a single-pitched baritone blast.

The diaphone is slightly more complicated. Its sound is produced by air passing through a slotted piston about six inches long and amplified by a resonator. It is considerably more versatile than the diaphragm and can be adjusted to produce two tones at varying intervals. The sound, in its simplest form, can be described according to one's aesthetic tastes. Some might compare it to a trumpet call ended by the note of a bass drum; others, more literal-minded, would call it a bellow and a grunt. Both descriptions, however, fail to do justice to the diaphone's variations and overtones, which give it a greater carrying quality than any other type horn.

The soprano tones in the bay's fog chorus are produced, appropriately enough, by sirens. Unlike most sirens, however, these are equipped with shutters which beneficently stifle the noise except during the prescribed interval. Thus the rising and falling wail heard in a fire siren, for example, is shut in, and only one pitch is heard.

Like most sopranos the bay's sirens are often temperamental. A shutter sometimes breaks down, and the siren looses a continuous nerve-shattering shriek which may go on for hours, riling the tempers of residents for miles around before it can be repaired. For this reason the sirens will probably ultimately be replaced, as they wear out, by the less troublesome baritone and bass-voiced diaphragms and diaphones. Thus, with the sopranos eliminated, the bay's chorus will be marked by less variety but greater dependability.

Valor in the Fog   One of the difficulties of a lighthouse keeper's life is accustoming his ears to the tremendous din of the horn. Fortunately the horn's resonator is always pointed away from the building. Nevertheless it is capable of rattling the windows and the dishes if not the keeper's back teeth. Even veterans of the service are careful to avoid exposure to the full force of the blast, which would doubtless result in damage to the eardrums. But the newcomer soon finds he can learn to sleep through the din. He is almost certain to awaken, however, when it stops.

The horns are spotted by type according to the needs of each station. The diaphones, loudest of the three, are given the most responsible positions, such as the outer Gate stations at Mile Rock and Point Bonita. Similarly, there is a double diaphone, one horn pointing bayward, the other seaward, just beneath the Golden Gate Bridge deck at exact center; and many a motorist driving the bridge in a fog for the first time has been startled to hear the immense blast going off apparently underneath his car.

When the bridge was first built, residents in San Francisco's nearby Sea Cliff district were jarred to near distraction by this horn's violent attack on their eardrums. In response to complaints a realignment of the horn's resonator turned the blast seaward and softened its impact on the city.

On the south pier of the bridge forty feet above the water is a double diaphragm horn, similarly oriented. Both bridge horns are controlled by the bridge's maintenance crews. Lime Point lighthouse, beneath the north tower, has a triple diaphragm—with an added feature; its horns sound simultaneously on different pitches, producing a musical chime effect. The Lime Point crew also operates by remote control a siren at the Point Diablo light on the north side of the Gate.

Besides these five the most conspicuous horns near San

Francisco are the single-toned diaphragms on either end of Alcatraz (only the south one can usually be heard from the city) and a picturesque diaphone on Yerba Buena with a particularly loud and tremulous blast, giving it an air of great age and authority. A number of sirens are spotted along the San Francisco docks and on the Bay Bridge.

Angel Island, besides having its two diaphragm horns, has a bell, which is the bay's oldest existing fog warning and has a history of its own. At the lighthouse on Point Knox at the southeast corner of the island Coast Guardsmen will point out to you the four-thousand-pound tocsin, which is now rung electrically. They will show you some tiny dents on it, which tell a story of persistence and valor.

Shortly after the turn of the century, when bells were still the only kind of fog signals, they were rung by mechanisms which had to be wound up periodically like a clock. The Point Knox lighthouse at that time was "manned" by a woman, Mrs. Juliet Nichols. During a particularly foggy spell in 1906 the hammer spring gave out, and Mrs. Nichols, fearful that ferries or other passing vessels would pile up on the island's rocky shores, found a hand hammer and began to pound the bell vigorously.

Throughout the day and night she swung her arm, hoping that the fog would lift. But it stayed—and she stayed—for an agonizing twenty-one consecutive hours. When the fog cleared, she got a few hours' rest until it came in again; and she renewed her vigil, swinging the hammer off and on for several days before relief came.

A similar tale of valor is told about the first operator of a fog signal in the bay area. In 1855 a retired Army sergeant named Maloney was hired to fire a cannon from Point Bonita every half hour during foggy weather. Possibly envisioning a non-strenuous job enabling him to relax at the end of his

Army career, Maloney was promptly besieged by some of the most persistent fogs on record.

With the dogged devotion to duty of an old soldier, he stuck to his post for two months, firing the cannon night and day, whenever the mists rolled in. Finally, he wrote a plea for help: "I cannot find any person here to relieve me, not five minutes; I have been up three days and nights and had only two hours rest . . . I was nearly used up. All the rest I would require in twenty-four hours is two if I only could get it."

Maloney shortly resigned his job, but his cannon is preserved as a relic in the Alameda Coast Guard Headquarters. Cannons were soon replaced by bells and steam whistles, and the first horns were installed about the time of World War I. Besides the historic bell on Angel Island other bells are still used in places where a very loud signal is not required, notably along waterfronts and on the piers of the Bay Bridge, supplementing its sirens.

All told, there are some thirty-five horns, sirens, and bells in the bay, operated each on the average of a thousand hours a year. Perhaps the most novel fog signals are the echo boards, used principally along the narrow curving channel through the delta to Stockton. By sounding his ship's whistle and timing for the echo, a pilot can ascertain his distance from the board.

A foghorn, particularly a diaphone, is capable of emitting what is probably the loudest sound—other than that from an explosion—made by man. Although the operating range of a diaphone is supposed to be four miles, it can often be heard for far greater distances. Strange effects result. It is not unusual for people strolling through Golden Gate Park in warm sunshine to hear the blast of the fog-shrouded Point Bonita diaphone five miles away, inaudible from points a mile or two closer in the lee of the Presidio hills.

The Bonita and Mile Rock signals can sometimes be heard

from areas on Mount Tamalpais some eight miles distant. Under extremely favorable conditions—no wind and exceptionally thick fog, which is a good sound conductor—the great diaphone of Bonita has been heard on ships ten miles at sea; and there are people who will swear they have heard the Golden Gate horns from the University of California campus in Berkeley, fourteen air-line miles from the bridge.

THE PASSING OF THE FERRIES

Probably never has any single mode of transportation so profoundly affected the life of a metropolitan community as the bay's ferryboats did in the era before the building of the bridges.

For more than three generations bay area residents by the tens of thousands sailed across the bay to work in San Francisco every morning and back again at night. But the ferry ride was far more than a means of getting to the job. It was a twice-daily social period, a convivial gathering, a respite in the day's routine only remotely approximated by the modern coffee break or the cocktail hour. In more than a figurative sense the passenger ferries were floating clubhouses. The regular commuters were members of well-defined in-groups with long-established totems, taboos, and folkways.

The Daily Voyage　　Each scheduled sailing had its own clan of passengers who caught the same boat at the same time, observing the same rituals, every working day in the year. By train, and to a lesser degree by automobile, they converged on the half-dozen main ferry terminals around the bay—at Alameda, Oakland, Berkeley, Richmond, Tiburon, and Sausalito. They rushed down the loading ramps a few minutes before sailing time, and some habitually went into the dining room for breakfast or to the lunch counter for coffee, others to the main cabin of the boat. Each had his regular seat, reserved for him not by any legal right but by immemorial custom—a tradition violated by a newcomer only at the risk of ostracism. The supreme offense was to take a seat left vacant by a commuter who recently had made his last long journey into the fog.

The rare passenger who spent the trip with his head buried in a newspaper was ostentatiously ignored. The only accepted use for a paper was to spread it across laps for a game of pinochle. Besides the card players there were the argument clubs, groups of half a dozen or so who carried on solemn debates—often lasting for several voyages or in some cases weeks and years—on such subjects as the latest political scandals, the current murder trial, the coming Big Game, the problem of where Drake landed, and the wisdom or folly of various plans to bridge the bay.

A newlywed returning to his regular place was inevitably the target for flying rice and mordant wit, and miserable was the lot of the new father who failed to distribute the traditional cigars. But the most merciless ribbing was reserved for a returning passenger who had decided not to sail on the previous day because of rough weather. On at least one occasion court was not held in San Francisco because the judge, a resident of Marin, had a queasy stomach and retreated from the rolling boat just before it sailed from the Sausalito dock.

A spontaneously organized male chorus on one of the Oakland boats regularly inflicted barbershop harmony on its captive audience. Passengers and crews habitually bandied insults regarding the abilities of the crewmen or the seaworthiness of the vessel, particularly in foggy or stormy weather. Veteran commuters were often practical jokers in the most elaborate tradition. A standard ritual involving a newcomer was to inform him that he was wanted on the telephone and send him off in search of nonexistent phone booths; or he would be approached by one of the regulars offering to sell him sea-gull insurance for twenty-five cents, in return for which he was guaranteed against any loss caused by the ferry's feathered convoy.

At the end of twenty-five to forty minutes (depending on the route and the weather) the leisurely interval was over. As the boat moved into the slip at San Francisco, passengers would jam the front end, swarm up the loading ramp, and hurry through the Ferry Building to the waiting streetcars at the foot of Market. At the end of the day the pattern was reversed; the office buildings of the city poured out their streams of commuters who flowed to the Ferry Building like rivers to the sea. On the evening voyage home the bars were opened up, and occasionally a passenger would become so engrossed that he inadvertently made two or three round trips before getting ashore.

There were living institutions aboard the ferries—great skippers like Captain John Leale, whose last voyage before his retirement in 1914 after a half century of service was hailed by whistle salutes from nearly every vessel on the bay; minor characters like the Chinese peanut vendor who distributed several million nuts to hungry commuters during his years on the boats; Eddie the one-legged sea gull, also known as Peg-Leg Pete; and the opera-loving deck hand who lustily warbled Verdi and Puccini arias for delighted passengers on the Sausalito ferries and so impressed musical authorities that he was asked to sing roles at the Opera House.

"Ferry Tales"   The Boswell of the boats was reporter Earle Ennis, who for many years conducted a regular column

in the San Francisco *Chronicle:* "Ferry Tales." He wrote nostalgically about the daily ride: ". . . the smell of coffee and snails, the thud of waves against the hull, the rhythmic pulse of the engines, the spray against the windows." Veteran commuters, wrote Ennis, "knew by the horns how thick the fog, by the cant of the boat how rough the bay, and by the rings in the pitchers how old the cream." They also sometimes took up collections for needy fellow passengers, quietly suppressed obstreperous drunks, helped stand lookout on foggy trips, and, on the rare occasions of collision in the fog, averted panic by treating the experience as if it were a staged prank.

The passing of the seasons was observed on the boats with appropriate folk customs. In the summer bathing-beauty contests were often staged on the decks; male commuters as judges would comment pointedly on the charms and contours of Miss Oakland as compared with those of Miss Milpitas, both of whom were usually shivering in the bay's brisk mid-summer zephyrs.

At the end of summer the more extravagant among the male passengers would take part in the annual ceremony of tossing overboard their straw hats. During Big Game week the commuters inevitably divided into two enemy camps, with spirited arguments, bets, and impromptu singing of Stanford and California songs by old grads who had forgotten most of the words.

During the week before Christmas the crews of various boats took a competitive pride in decking out their vessels with yuletide greenery. Passengers organized committees to supply and decorate Christmas trees, and to the accompaniment of carol singing Santa Claus would appear with such gifts from the company as celluloid commute book covers.

Under these circumstances it is understandable that the long-time commuters developed a deep fondness for the ferries. Perhaps the ultimate in devotion was revealed one evening on one of the Marin-bound boats as the sun was going down behind the Golden Gate. A passenger went to the rail on the upper deck and dumped overboard what appeared to be a bucket of debris of some kind. To his consternation the wind from the Gate blew most of the dusty substance back onto the boat, where some of it lodged in the eyes and noses of other passengers. They indignantly demanded to know what the big idea was. The offender apologized profusely and explained that he was disposing of the ashes of a late-lamented commuter—known to all—who had requested that his remains be scattered from the ferry into the Golden Gate at sunset. The abashed passengers quickly expressed their regrets, removed their hats, and stood in silent tribute to their departed comrade and his final trip across the waters.

Murder on the Upper Deck   In the days before the bridges the ferries provided the most obvious means of self-destruction for would-be suicides. But walking off a ferryboat usually proved to be a highly unsatisfactory method. Often the jumper would change his mind upon hitting the frigid water, or would at least be so shocked by the icy bath that the normal human instinct to keep breathing would overcome his determination to destroy himself.

With few exceptions the only would-be suicides who accomplished their purpose were those who stepped off near the bow of a boat and were struck by the paddle wheel or propeller. Captain John Leale, however, told of one instance of a jumper who stepped straight over the bow, disappeared under the boat, and shortly bobbed up astern, where he was fished out, disgruntled but unharmed.

On another occasion a passenger jumped off in mid-bay at night and was not missed; on the same ferry's return trip, an hour and a half later, the captain saw something floating in the water, pulled it out, and recognized his former passenger, alive, shivering, and grateful to be saved from freezing.

Much of the drama that took place on the decks of the ferries went unsung, but at least one birth, one marriage, and one murder found their way into the records.

The birth took place on a ferry skippered by Captain Enos Fouratt: "A woman came up to me on deck," he related some years later, "and pointed to another woman on the bench.

" 'She's going to have a baby,' she said.

"I said, 'When?'

"She said, 'Right now!'

"Well, I asked if there was a doctor on board. There wasn't. It was up to me, although I had no idea what to do. . . .

"About five years later a lady came aboard with a little girl by the hand and said: 'I guess you don't remember me, Captain . . .'"

One time at the Ferry Building a dewy-eyed young couple arrived on the boat with a minister in tow and asked Captain John Leale if they could be married aboard. Although the bewhiskered skipper was noted for his adherence to strict discipline aboard his vessel, he finally gave in to the entreaties of the couple and even invited them to hold the ceremony inside the ferryboat's sanctum, the pilothouse, with the proviso that the captain be allowed to kiss the bride. After the mid-bay ceremony the skipper solemnly claimed his price, strode to the whistle cord, and pulled it till the bay echoed with the glad tidings.

The ferryboat murder was one of the most celebrated homicide cases in San Francisco history. The central character was a widow of renown, glamour, and fiery temperament, appropriately named Laura D. Fair. For some years during the 1860s she carried on a tempestuous love affair with a married attorney named Alexander Crittenden, a member of one of the city's most prominent families.

Late in 1870 Crittenden decided to break off with Mrs. Fair and asked his wife, who had gone East, to return to him. Mrs. Crittenden relented and planned to return to the city. On November 3, Crittenden boarded the ferry *El Capitan* and crossed the bay to meet her at the train in Oakland. Unknown to him, his jilted mistress followed him aboard the boat.

With a natural instinct for timing Laura Fair shrewdly waited for the most dramatic moment. As the reunited couple walked to the *El Capitan's* upper deck for the return to the city, she stepped from the shadows of the deckhouse, pulled out a small pistol, and fired point blank. Crittenden slumped to the deck, fatally wounded.

The trial of Laura Fair was one of the sensations of a spectacular era. Militant suffragettes regarded her action as justifiable exercise of a woman's inalienable rights against the man who had done her wrong. For months before and during the trial the case was hotly debated in ferryboats, in taverns, and across dinner tables, with the lines frequently drawn according to sex. Mrs. Fair was visited in her cell by those two vigorous fighters for women's rights, Elizabeth Stanton and Susan B. Anthony. After a long and lurid trial she was convicted, sentenced to the gallows, granted a new trial, and finally acquitted on grounds of "emotional insanity."

The Bay's Fleet   The origin of the bay's ferries is deeply embedded in legend. Stories are told of a fierce Indian chief (to the tellers of tales all Indians are chiefs) who refused to yield to the invading Spanish and withdrew to the larger of the two small islands off San Rafael. He was finally captured and baptized at Mission San Rafael, but instead of settling down to a life of menial toil at the mission, as did his fellow tribesmen, the enterprising red man went into business. He put to use his native knowledge of the bay's winds and currents by building a boat and ferrying paying passengers across the Golden Gate.

The Spanish labeled him Marino or El Marinero (the Sailor), later shortened to Marin, and the name was applied to his island and subsequently to the entire peninsula north of the Gate.

The first regularly scheduled trips across the bay were made in 1850 by the little propeller-driven steamer *Kangaroo*, lineal ancestor of the modern ferries. It was operated twice weekly by Captain Thomas Gray, who piloted his vessel, weather permitting, from San Francisco to San Antonio Creek, now the Oakland Estuary.

Soon afterward hustling Gold Rush entrepreneurs established regular ferry lines to Marin and other bay points and carried gold seekers up through the delta to Stockton and Sacramento. Railroad companies, which began to operate around the bay, soon found it to their advantage to connect their lines with San Francisco by establishing their own ferry systems.

When a Central Pacific locomotive chugged into Oakland-Alameda in 1869 with the bay area's first overland train, the railroad ferried its passengers across to San Francisco, establishing a tradition fortunately still followed. Central Pacific was the parent of the present Southern Pacific, which became the largest operator of ferryboats on the bay and probably in the world. Entire trains, cut into sections, were rolled directly onto the boats and floated across the bay.

Many other types of ferries and river boats plowed the waters of the bay: stern-wheelers, side-wheelers, and propeller-driven craft; oil burners and coal burners; single-enders and double-enders; auto ferries and passenger ferries. Long piers, trestles, and moles were built out from East Bay shores to reach deep water where the boats could dock.

In 1898 San Francisco's towered Ferry Building was constructed to handle the immense traffic. At the height of the ferry era some fifty million passengers a year trod its echoing corridors—reportedly more than those handled by any other depot in the world except London's Charing Cross Station. It was one of the few buildings in San Francisco substantially undamaged by the earthquake and fire of 1906, and thousands of people were able to leave the blazing city by ferry for refuge across the bay.

Competition for the giant S.P.—Southern Pacific—came later from several sources, including the Key System, which operated passenger ferries only. The company was so named because of the key-shaped route of the East Bay electric train lines it built to haul passengers to the boats.

Although sailings were sometimes delayed by fog and roughened by wind, the ferries had a remarkable record of maintaining schedules without accident, particularly in view of the fact that there were as many as fifty boats operating on the bay at one time. The *San Rafael* was rammed by another boat in a fog off Alcatraz in 1901, the only fatal ferry collision on record, although two other boats, the *Sehome* and the *Golden City*, were sunk without loss of life, and there were many near misses.

Occasionally a boat would run aground in the fog, and at rare intervals the bay in a mood of fury would buffet a ferry like a toy. On Christmas morning of 1921 the *Charles Van Damme*, sailing from Point San Quentin for Richmond, was struck by a strong southeaster. The vessel pitched in the heavy sea and made little headway. Then came the contingency dreaded by all seamen—a broken rudder. Her automobile deck awash, the *Van Damme* drifted helplessly in the gale. A lifeboat was blown loose from its davits and smashed a car. The funnel, its guys broken, swayed ominously in every gust, pulling the whistle cord as it did so. Passengers huddled together in life jackets, and one man strapped life preservers to his car. Five hours after leaving San Quentin the *Van Damme* was finally safely anchored near Richmond without casualties after the roughest day in the memory of bay boatmen.

The End of the Line   With the coming of the bridges and their train and bus service the ferries were doomed. On the morning of January 14, 1939, the ferryboat *Piedmont*, with a capacity load of three thousand aboard, set out from Alameda at eight o'clock on the final voyage of the last East Bay commuter ferry. There were no card games that morning, and there was only one subject of conversation from stem to stern. Black-clad "pallbearers" at the mock funeral passed out crying towels, and serpentin was tossed from the deck to the wharf as the boat left the dock.

Banners of famous ferries from the *Kangaroo* to the *Piedmont* were displayed. The oldest commuters gravely informed everyone that in the early days the fog was always thicker and the waves much higher. Some passengers yielded to a long-frustrated urge to jerk the dangling cords which released the life preservers. Many joined hands and sang "Auld Lang Syne."

The bay's shores echoed to the whistles of other vessels blowing salutes to the last of the commuter boats. Solemnly the *Piedmont's* whistle responded. And when the old sidewheeler docked at the Ferry Building, there was not the usual rush to the ramps. Many a passenger lingered aboard, reluctant to ring down the curtain on an unforgettable era.

Some of the boats, including the *Piedmont*, enjoyed a brief reprieve, carrying passengers to the exposition on Treasure Island in the summers of 1939 and 1940. Many were commandeered by the government during the war to transport troops and shipyard workers around the bay. A few auto ferries continued on their runs long after the building of the two big bridges. The Richmond–San Rafael line operated four boats until the completion of the bridge over that route in September of 1956. The Martinez–Benicia run, which was said to be the oldest ferry service west of the Mississippi, also continued, although doomed by the planned construction of a new bridge over the route. (The emblem of the latter line was a martini glass; according to legend, the cocktail originated as the "Martinez" in the town of that name.)

The S.P. continued to operate two boats from Oakland to San Francisco for the convenience of its train passengers— the Key System's old *San Leandro* and the ancient *Berkeley*, with its stained-glass windows. The venerable *Eureka*, last of the side-wheelers and largest of all the double-end ferries, was taken out of service early in 1957 and presented to San Francisco's Maritime Museum at Aquatic Park.

Twice during strikes which idled the Bay Bridge trains in 1947 and 1953, the S.P. ferried boatloads of passengers to work, and the old days of the commuter boats were briefly revived. But lack of regular bus or train connections to the Oakland terminal made the trip a long and impractical one.

Many a bay area resident will long treasure the memory of weekend moonlight rides across the bay and up the Sacramento River on the steamboats, with music, dancing, and the hum and swoosh of the ponderous stern wheels. The last of the passenger-carrying river boats were the *Delta King* and *Delta Queen*, which during the 1920s and '30s made overnight trips from San Francisco to Sacramento. The latter now makes similar trips up the Mississippi and Ohio.

Even into the 1940s the river boat *Petaluma* continued to chug up Petaluma Slough on her nightly thirty-eight-mile trip to her namesake city, bringing back eggs and poultry for the tables of San Franciscans. But in 1950 a barge took over the run, and the old stern-wheeler went into retirement—California's last steamboat. She became more famous in retirement, however, than she had been in active service. The *Petaluma* was moored in the Oakland Estuary at Jack London Square as the Showboat restaurant until she burned to the water's edge in 1956.

Several of the ferries were converted into restaurants and clubhouses, the *Encinal* at Benicia, the *Tamalpais* at Antioch, and the *Newark* in San Diego. The *Cazadero* had the most spectacular fate; she was used by the Navy for demolition practice and was blown up near Hunters Point. The *Peralta* was converted into the swank streamliner *Kalakala,* running out of Seattle. And the *Yosemite* steamed out the Gate and headed for South America, where she was put on the thirty-three-mile run between Buenos Aires and Montevideo.

Legacy   "They ought to bring back the ferries" is an inevitable observation whenever the problem of traffic congestion on the bridges is discussed. Letters regularly appear in the bay area newspapers demanding that the boats be returned to service and arguing that the slowest boat could not take more time than is required to inch across the Bay Bridge at rush hour.

Officials claim that the return of the commuter ferries would be uneconomical. They assert that the demand to bring back the boats—like the fight to preserve San Francisco's cable cars—is motivated more by sentiment than by a hard-headed analysis of the economics of transportation. In this respect they may be right. But it is understandable that sentiment plays a part in the attitude of bay area residents toward the ferries. For the boats were a unique social institution. Admittedly they lacked speed and efficiency, but they also lacked some other elements of more modern forms of transportation—the high-tension frenzy of rush-hour car commuting, the nerve-fraying lane-to-lane infighting among drivers who know each other not as human beings but only by make and model.

On the ferries commuters were brought together in a world of their own, knowing something of the intimacy that comes only between passengers on the same water voyage of whatever duration, sharing the common experience of isolation from the outside world, even if only for a few minutes. There was leisure on a ferry trip, time for unhurried conversation, time to wander about the decks, to feed the gulls, or to stand at the rail and contemplate the changing patterns in the moving water or the cities along the shores.

A crossing in fog or storm was a special occasion; then more than ever the passengers felt bound together in the unspoken mutuality that comes of being "in the same boat," facing the same perils, however remote.

To the ferry commuters the bay was more than a fragmentary glimpse of blue water in the distance; it was a direct experience, a working part of their lives. Every morning and every evening they smelled its salt spray from the deck, heard the sound of its waves, breathed its cool winds off the water, sensed its changes as the boat moved in response to the tides and currents.

The intimate experience of the boat ride, of the bay and its changing beauty created a mood of easygoing friendliness, geniality, and camaraderie which undoubtedly helped mold the character of the community. Quite possibly San Francisco's reputation as a city of serenity and of vision is due in some degree to the effect on three generations of that twice-daily journey across the waters.

AUTUMN

There is an incomparable day that comes once a year on the bay.

It arrives not according to any man-made calendar, but like the date of Easter is determined by what happens in the sky. Like Easter, too, it is a day of awakening, but it comes always in the fall of the year. It is the first clear day after the first rain.

Early autumn, like early spring, is a time of soft haze, of muted colors, of peace and somnolence. Then, perhaps without warning, the rains come. They may come in a series of showers or in a drenching downpour; they may last for a day or for a week; but their aftermath is the same.

One morning the rains are gone; the mists are washed away; and with a sudden crescendo the bay is brilliant with new life. The wind is sharp and cold; the air sparkles like burnished glass; the bay radiates with an intensity of light not seen since winter. The cliffs and rocks of the Golden Gate are fringed with white breakers, and the light glitters and dances across the cobalt surface, flecked with whitecaps like coconut on a cake.

The great bridge at the strait, which for months has been a vaguely floating outline in the fogs and mists and clouds, now leaps again from shore to shore with incredible intensity and vividness, each of its harp-string cables, every chord of its steel-webbed deck, every sculptured ridge of its sky-reaching towers eloquently vibrant in the morning sun. A glint of light is reflected from the windshield of a car on its deck, and answering flashes come from the deck of the Bay Bridge ten miles across the water.

All the bay seems to sing in the morning light, in the sharp invigorating radiance of this superlative moment of the year. Around its shores three million people are going to work, feeling in their pulses the quickening splendor of this shining day.

7

The Living Waters

Commuters on a Berkeley ferry one day in 1934 were startled
to see the shape of a huge animal rise from the water not far
from the boat. It submerged again before it could be identified, but some of the passengers were convinced that they had
seen a sea monster.

A few days later the same or a similar "monster" was
spotted off Richmond. Unfortunately no one had any cameras
handy at either appearance and there were no experts present to identify the beast, so the bay's only monster legend will
always be unauthenticated. Although it is possible that the
observers' imaginations were working overtime, it is also possible that the "monster" label was not far wrong. Rare
varieties of whales and other giants of the deep have been
found in the bay, and how many others cruise these waters
unseen will never be known.

Only at such rare intervals when a strange form of life penetrates the surface does it come to public notice that the bay contains more than water. Actually no major city in the Western world is in such close contact with primitive life on a large scale as is San Francisco. In terms of the density of animal life it is as if the city were enclosed on three sides by the jungles of the Amazon. Though three million people live around the bay's shores, the non-human population of the bay itself is at least a million times as great.

If the bay were transparent, it would be possible, looking into its depths, to peer back through time and view a pageant of evolution illustrating the progress of life from its earliest forms up to the point when it emerged from its first home in the waters to take up residence on dry land.

Beneath the passing traffic of ships and small boats, in the dim lower regions unknown to shore dwellers, the elemental forms of marine life ebb and flow as they have for aeons before the arrival of man, living each moment on the razor edge of existence between survival and oblivion.

In submerged valleys far below the bridges where commuters ride in glass-enclosed comfort, mussel larvae are eaten by clams which are devoured by bristle worms which are gulped by bat rays which are preyed upon by sharks. Octopi lurk in rocky caverns, and big crabs reach out with spiny arms to devour whatever luckless smaller creatures may swim within reach.

Residents of the Bay Floor   Scoop up a bucketful of water from anywhere in the bay, and the chances are good that it is swarming with plankton—minute organisms of many varieties, some barely visible, some microscopic. The plankton includes the progenitor of all animal life—the Protozoa, literally "first animals." This is the Beginning. Between the single cell of the Protozoa, drifting at random in the bay's waves and deeps, and the single human being standing on its shore, lies a gap of more than a billion years.

A slightly lesser gap separates man from another form of life in the plankton, the larvae, jellyfish-like substances which are the first stage in the development of many marine animals. If a mollusk larva, for example, is lucky enough to escape the gaping jaws of hungry fish, it will settle down on a rock or sandy bottom, grow a shell, and become a full-fledged clam, mussel, oyster, or snail. It may then turn the tables and devour other passing larvae with no discrimination whatever, often cannibalistically making meals from the larvae of its own species.

In some areas of the bay the mollusks are so prolific that they grow in beds many feet deep, and their shelled remains carpet the bay floor. In the south bay, for example, oyster shells are dredged from beds which may be thirty feet thick.

Of all the forms of animal life in the bay the champion breeder and holder of all population records is the tiny jewel clam, named for its size rather than any other resemblance to a gem. Like other clams it prefers muddy bottoms, but unlike many other varieties it is too small to attract the most voracious predators of all—humans. The succulent littlenecked clams, up to four inches long, are far more vulnerable and are scooped up in bucketloads by clam diggers when minus tides leave bare the mud flats around the bay's edges at places like Richardson Bay in Marin and Coyote Point near San Mateo. This variety was doubtless responsible for the proverb about the happiness of a clam at high tide. Steamed or chowdered, it makes a tasty dish.

Visitors walking on the bay's shores at low tide are sometimes puzzled by the appearance of two odd and apparently unrelated phenomena: tiny geysers of water spouting from the sand and sea gulls which appear to be smoking cigars.

Both are evidence of the presence of the largest of the bay's clams, a giant species which may almost reach the size of a football and burrows down in the mud to a depth of two feet. It sucks in water from the surface by means of a long, cigar-shaped tube, strains out its own nourishment, and squirts the water out again in a sudden short jet. The tubes are prized as food by the gulls, which often make off with them without regard to the requirements of the owners.

A clue to one of the great mysteries of marine life—the migrations of fish—may be found in the behavior of one of the clam's near relatives, the mussel. The bay mussel, a black-shelled mollusk which clamps itself firmly to rocks or pilings, is a species distinct from those outside the Gate, and its spawn forms one of the most important food sources for the bay's fish. In the spring, influenced by unknown forces—possibly changes in the bay's salinity or temperature—it throws out vast quantities of cells called gametes, which combine to form the mussel larvae. Biologists speculate that this great seasonal larva production of the mussels may determine in some degree the migrations of the fish which depend on it for food.

Another variety, the horse mussel, is helping to diminish the size of the bay. It grows in colonies on the mud flats, protrudes above the shallow bottom an inch or two, and creates a dead space of water where there are no currents to carry away the silt. Seeds land in the silt, grow up into marsh grasses, and create more dead space for the deposit of more silt, eventually making the mud flats a marsh and the marsh a dry meadow. Thus the horse mussel, by eliminating its own environment, appears determined to commit race suicide.

In a more literal sense this hungry mollusk often bites off more than it can chew. Birds such as the California clapper rail, wading in shallow water, sometimes inadvertently place a foot in an open mussel shell. The bird may leave, but the foot stays, trapped by the closing of the shell like a vise.

Scuttling across the bay floor at all depths are dozens of kinds of crabs, including the famed hermit crab, a small variety which takes up residence in the discarded shells of other animals, principally snails. In his choice of a home the hermit is not too discriminating, however, and will accept a low-grade substitute; in captivity he can be satisfied with a metal ring around his middle, apparently under the delusion that he is comfortably housed in a shell.

Even more renowned than the hermit is another crustacean, the *Crago franciscorum,* the bay's own unique form of shrimp. Hauled up in fish nets by the millions, this tiny bottom dweller is prized by many gourmets as far more tender and tasty than the bigger ocean-going shrimp. Humans are not alone in their appreciation of the savory *Crago franciscorum;* it forms a staple item in the diet of most of the bay's fish population.

Particularly fond of shrimp is an odd inhabitant of the bay floor, the flatfish, which might also be called the fish with the wandering eye. He belongs to a large family—of which the flounder and the turbot are most numerous in the bay—and like any other fish comes into the world with eyes in the normal place on each side of his head. Within two weeks one eye begins to migrate to the other side of the head, and at the age of three weeks both eyes are on the same side. The fish then turns his blind side to the bottom and spends the rest of his life looking up. He often slithers beneath a thin layer of sand with only his bulging eyes above the surface and, thus camouflaged, lies in wait for a tender shrimp to pass by.

Dangerous Customers   During World War I unexplained disasters began to strike harbor installations. Piers with loaded freight cars collapsed into the bay, and ferry wharves began to fall apart. Enemy action was suspected. Investigation proved that the bay had indeed been invaded by an enemy—the shipworm, or teredo. This clamlike mollusk, which had plagued mariners since the times of the Greeks and Romans by burrowing into the hulls of wooden vessels, had developed an insatiable appetite for the bay's wooden pilings.

Old pilings were replaced by new ones chemically treated to resist the hungry shipworm, but not before the little mollusks had gobbled up millions of dollars' worth of wharves. The shipworm problem is still an acute one in those areas above Carquinez where pilings originally built in fresh water —in which the shipworm cannot live—are attacked by the animals in dry seasons when the river flow diminishes and the salt water advances.

The bay mollusk with the most fearsome reputation is the octopus. Paradoxically, he is one of the shiest of the bay's inhabitants, usually hides in deep rocky crevices, and will avoid a fight if he can possibly run away—or squirt away: when he is in a hurry he travels head first, legs together and trailing, jet-propelled as he squirts water to the rear. If chased, he will confuse his pursuer by emitting a cloud of octopus "ink" as a smoke screen.

Octopi are not numerous in the bay, and most of them are small, measuring less than two feet across with tentacles outspread. Some grow larger, however; one, found wrapped around a piling at the Bethlehem Steel plant in South San Francisco, measured seven and a half feet in diameter—about as big as they come.

The octopus' two large eyes bear an uncanny resemblance to human eyes, and the brain behind them is surprisingly large, making him the smartest creature on the bay floor, able to stalk his prey with cunning and resourcefulness, sometimes heaving rocks at hapless mollusks.

Normally harmless to man, when driven to combat the octopus is capable of putting up a deadly fight. His most potent weapon is not in his long tentacles but a sharp beak capable of inflicting a poisonous bite.

Considerably more to be feared than the octopus, however, is the deadly bat sting ray, which is sometimes confused with the harmless skate because both are flat-bodied and have wide flopping "wings." The sting ray is fully capable of living up to his name. He has a "wingspread" often reaching four feet and possesses a stinging spine, sometimes several inches long, which can inflict a poisonous and extremely painful wound. His powerful teeth are well suited for crushing mollusks; he has a particular fondness for oysters—an appetite primarily responsible for the fences built around the bay's old commercial oyster beds.

An even more ingenious weapon than the bat ray's stinger is wielded by his cousin, the electric ray, possessor of a built-in battery capable of sending out a jolt that will knock a man off his feet. His scientific name, appropriately enough, is *Torpedo californica*. Anyone wading in the bay's marshes will do well to keep an eye out for members of the inhospitable ray family.

Singers, Stripers, and Whoppers　　Although no one has ever taken a census of the bay's fish, the nearest approximation was a tally kept over a period of several years by California Academy of Sciences biologists. They enumerated fish caught in the nets of Chinese shrimp fishermen off Oakland and in the screens of the Pacific Gas and Electric Company's steam plant in San Francisco. Altogether more than seventy species have been identified. Varieties not caught in either place would possibly bring the total close to one hundred.

The population record is held by the surf perches, which

far outnumber all other fish together. A peculiarity of these little fish, seldom more than a few inches long, is that they lay no eggs but are viviparous, bearing their young alive—a fact which amazed the biological world when it was first discovered in this bay many years ago.

Ranking second is the staghorn sculpin, often called the "bullhead," followed in numbers by the Pacific herring, which enter the bay in great schools in the winter to spawn, leaving large areas of the surface coated with their eggs; the bocaccio, a "rock cod" whose name literally means "big mouth"; the San Francisco topsmelt; the tom cod; the midshipman; and the striped bass.

The midshipman is the bay's most talented fish. His name comes from a series of spots along his body which vaguely resemble the brass buttons of a midshipman's uniform. But the fish has one ability the naval student might well envy: he can light up his buttons like a Christmas tree.

There are 658 of these light organs, enough to furnish sufficient illumination to read a newspaper. Presumably the lights were not developed for this purpose, but no one is certain exactly what their function is. It is speculated that they may be recognition lights, enabling one of the species to locate another for romantic reasons. Perhaps the lights also serve to illuminate the midshipman's face—one of the ugliest possessed by any creature of the seas—and thereby terrify his enemies.

This versatile fish has other talents, too. He is also called, with good reason, the California singing fish. Walk around on some of the bay's rocky shores at low tide in June or July and you may hear his "song"—a throaty rasp that has been variously described as a growl, a croak, and a grunt. The noise comes from the male fish, which has been left to guard the nestful of eggs under a rock, leaving the female free to rove. When he is off duty, however, swimming around with other members of the family, his song changes to a paternal purr.

Another bay oddity is the pipefish, which actually looks less like a pipe than a miniature fire hose with its head as the nozzle. He swims around, often vertically, among the grass of the marshes, imitating the vegetation. Like the midshipman, the male pipefish has certain domestic duties; his mate lays her eggs in what amounts to his vest pocket. Cozily ensconced there, the young hatch and are nurtured until they can venture out on their own. Sometimes the watery world outside is too much for them, and they retreat from danger to the safety of their father's breadbasket.

The special delight of bay anglers is the striped bass, an involuntary immigrant from the Atlantic coast. Stripers were introduced by fish-and-game authorities in 1879, when 132 of them were brought in by railroad from New Jersey and dumped into the bay at Martinez. Three years later another 300 were imported. So prolific were those 432 fish and their descendants that bay anglers now catch a million and a half or more every year without making a dent in the population.

The tasty stripers are strictly a sport fish, protected by law from commercial fishermen. They are a long-lived species; one lucky enough to escape the hook may live more than twenty years and attain a respectable size. Although those hauled in by anglers average ten pounds, twenty- and thirty-pounders are taken in large numbers, and the biggest striper on record weighed in at seventy-eight.

Their summer feeding grounds range through Carquinez Strait, the northern part of the bay, and the Golden Gate. Then in the fall most of them move east in great masses to winter in the fresh water of the central delta. With the coming of spring the procreative urge sends them traveling once more, this time to the outer reaches of the delta to spawn;

some swim short distances up tributary rivers. Then they head downstream for the bay again.

Although the stripers' wanderlust may have something to do with seasonal changes in the food supply, their migration has never been fully explained, any more than has that of a far more extensive traveler, the salmon. Silvery schools of king salmon used to enter the Gate and head up the Sacramento against the currents into headwaters sometimes hundreds of miles from the ocean, battling rapids, leaping falls. But the construction of dams along most major California rivers has cut the salmon migration to a trickle. Fish "ladders" are seldom very effective. The dams have also curtailed the wanderings of such other migrants as shad and steelhead.

Another traveler, the sturgeon, seems to have been unaffected by the barriers, probably because his great bulk prevents him from getting that far upstream anyhow. He is the largest creature of any kind normally found in the bay, a huge horny-skinned fish with a head resembling that of a crocodile.

For many years sturgeons were a dwindling race, but legal protection resulted in a population increase to the point that they can again be lawfully caught by anglers. A limit of one fish per angler was imposed, but one is usually enough. After reeling in a one-hundred-pound fighting sturgeon a fisherman is glad to call it a day. The largest ever caught locally was a giant hauled out of Suisun Bay weighing a whopping thirteen hundred pounds.

Sharks and Whales   Sharks patrol the bay in considerable numbers, and although there are no records of attacks on human swimmers here, they are the scourge of the underwater world, preying voraciously on virtually every other form of life, even including giant bat rays.

At the Coyote Point Shark Derby, a recreational event sponsored by civic organizations, about two thousand sharks of various species are caught annually by contestants in a single day's haul. The most vicious species in the bay is probably the seven-gill shark, capable of giving a bad time to any fisherman brave enough to pull him in, lashing out with his sharp teeth on anything within reach, including oars and the sides of the boat.

Other species of sharks are more populous in the bay: the brown smoothhound and the leopard, both of which make good eating but seldom show up on the menus at Fisherman's Wharf, probably because of an unfounded belief that a shark's meat is as tough as his disposition; the dogfish, which attacks his victims by curling up like a bow and lashing out with his poisonous spines; and the soup-fin, which enters the bay only in season to drop its young. The latter species, depleted seriously during recent years when its liver was the major source of vitamin A, now enjoys the protection of the law.

In the bay few of these species attain a length of more than six feet. But other bay sharks range larger; the biggest ever caught by an angler was an eleven-foot, 464-pound six-gill hauled in near Sausalito. An even larger specimen, an eighteen-foot, half-grown basking shark—a type which seldom comes here—got fouled up in the shipyards at Hunters Point in 1953.

Occasionally another rare shark has been found in the bay, the thresher, which may reach a length of eight feet and has a long, scythe-shaped tail which he wields as a weapon, swinging it in big arcs, threshing the water to herd smaller fish within reach of his teeth. The thresher's spectacular method of combat is probably responsible for the legend that in the open ocean he will team up with swordfish and attack whales. There is no evidence to support the story; even the most vicious shark is no match for the monsters of the deep.

Although whales of any variety do not normally enter the

bay, sometimes a California gray whale will stray from the route of his tribe's regular migrations along the coast and wander in through the Gate, spouting and sounding to the delight—and often anxiety—of boatmen. Another variety, the humpback, enters the bay in a less dignified manner. The big mammals are killed by whalers off the Farallones, strapped alongside a ship, and hauled to a converted sardine cannery at Point San Pablo, the only whaling station in the United States. There they suffer the further indignity of being converted into food for commercially raised mink.

The largest creature ever found in the bay or its approaches was a mammoth whale weighing possibly sixty tons, which washed ashore at Land's End in a storm in May of 1919. The stench of the decomposing leviathan was carried for miles on the wind. Towed to sea, the carcass stubbornly returned with the tide and finally had to be burned. The species was not identified, but it was probably a sperm whale belonging to the same tribe as Melville's Moby-Dick. A smaller specimen of the same species was beached near the same spot in 1938. In May of 1952 a beaked whale, an extremely rare species, was washed up on a mud flat near the Bay Bridge toll plaza; only a half-dozen of this variety had been found anywhere in the world. Where it came from or was bound for remains a mystery.

The most fun-loving of the bay's inhabitants is the whale's smaller relative, the porpoise. ". . . He always swims in hilarious shoals," wrote Melville. ". . . If you yourself can withstand three cheers at beholding these vivacious fish, then heaven help ye; the spirit of godly gamesomeness is not in ye."

Swimming with remarkable co-ordination, the porpoises put on a show like a water ballet, breaking the surface with a smooth rolling motion, diving, splashing, and blowing with energetic exuberance. Sometimes a group of them will simultaneously rise partly out of the water in such a way as to give the appearance of being a sea serpent—an illusion that could possibly have been responsible for the 1934 "sea monster" rumors.

Free or in captivity they are incurable exhibitionists. Although no bay porpoises have ever been trained, members of the same family have been taught to leap fifteen or twenty feet out of the water, snatching fish, blowing horns, and playing a modified form of basketball.

Shore Dwellers   The most publicized mammals in the bay area are the inhabitants of Seal Rocks, off the Cliff House. To the Spaniards they were *lobos marinos*—sea wolves—and their name was given to Point Lobos. Actually they are neither wolves nor seals but Steller sea lions. The only genuine seals in the bay are the much smaller leopard seals, who like to bask on beaches and sand bars—such as Seal Island near the Bay Bridge toll plaza—but usually leave Seal Rocks to their big cousins. The latter may weigh as much as a ton and do not bark like a seal but emit a roar as fearful as that of their jungle namesakes. The most photographed member of the Seal Rocks tribe was one big bull who somehow managed to get his head stuck through a wooden toilet seat and wore it as a permanent collar.

Most of the sea lions leave Seal Rocks in May and June for their breeding grounds on Año Nuevo Island twenty-five miles south or on the Farallones. There the bulls engage in elephantine battles for their harems. After bearing the young, the cows teach them to swim for the trip back to Seal Rocks in late summer or early fall.

There is a story that the inhabitants of the rocks were so alarmed by the earthquake of 1906 that they departed for the Farallones and did not come back for several seasons. It is probable, however, that after the big shake, which occurred in April, most of them simply left on their customary trek to the breeding grounds and their return at the usual time was unnoticed by San Franciscans, who were too busy rebuilding to observe wild life.

Normally a goodly number of the animals do not migrate at breeding time (they're either too young or too old) but remain in the vicinity all year, for the benefit of summer tourists—and mariners. Early editions of the *Pacific Coast Pilot*—the guide for mariners published by the U. S. Coast and Geodetic Survey—noted that, although there were no fog signals on Point Lobos, the dangerous rocks offshore were equipped with natural foghorns—the continual roaring of the sea lions.

Around the bay's wilder shores are great numbers of land-going mammals. In Marin County the raccoons come to the water's edge, usually by night, for fish, crabs, and other sea food. They are excellent swimmers, a fact doubtless responsible for the naming of Raccoon Strait, between Angel Island and Tiburon.

Surprisingly, the deer of that vicinity are also good swimmers. The Angel Island herd, some fifty Columbia blacktails whose ancestors were brought to the island about 1915, is particularly at home in the water. Although they have been known to take to the bay when pursued, there is no solid evidence for the legend that at certain times of the year they migrate to and from the mainland by swimming the half mile across Raccoon Strait. At slack water the strait would be an easy paddle for the animals, but unless they have evolved some special means of predicting the tides, they would risk being swept helplessly into the open bay by the powerful currents.

Among the islands and marshes of the delta mink roam wild and are trapped for their pelts. Energetic beavers swim in the delta's marshes and canals, and their excavations are such a menace to the levees that irate farmers have formed a Beaver Control District to curb the damage. The sea otter, once abundant in the bay, was slaughtered by the thousands in the early part of the nineteenth century. Fur hunters—Russians as well as Americans and British—were reported to have killed an average of more than one hundred a day. Although long believed to be extinct, the otters have made a small-scale comeback on the coast and have been seen in some numbers south of Monterey. Conceivably they might someday return to the bay, though scarcely in the numbers that lured the Russians.

Air-borne Residents   A fascinating link in the bay's evolutionary scale is the cormorant. Observers are sometimes surprised to see a snaky neck and head scooting along in the water as if it belonged to some fast-swimming reptile. The cormorant's black body floats so low that it is scarcely visible. He may dive for a fish, disappear for perhaps a minute, then emerge gradually, trailing his tail in the water and beating his wings violently to get enough speed to become air-borne.

His meal finished, he is likely to perch on a rock, wings outspread, waving them slowly to dry, as if being in the water like a lower form of life were really a distasteful business he would prefer to forget. At low tide Alcatraz rock, just west of the island, is a favorite perching spot.

Great flocks of these birds can often be seen flying low over the water in single file, wings beating swiftly, heading for their roosting areas at such places as Brooks Island and Red Rock, where they congregate by the thousands.

The cormorants are the birds exploited in the Orient by fishermen, who keep them on a leash; a noose around the bird's neck prevents him from swallowing the fish he catches, and the fisherman retrieves it. Any fisherman attempting this practice in the bay, however, would doubtless hear from the S.P.C.A.

At the opposite end of the scale from the primitive cormorant is the glamour bird of the bay, the egret. This tall white member of the heron family can often be seen wading in the shallow areas around Richardson Bay Bridge and on similar marshy shores. The big bird often reaches three feet in height and has long white plumes, a near-fatal attraction. The feathers were long used as adornments for ladies' hats, causing the birds to be hunted almost to extinction. Legal protection—and changing fashions in headgear—eventually allowed the birds to make a comeback.

The marshes frequented by the egrets are rapidly being filled for subdivisions, however, and many of the birds, like the Indians before them, have retreated to an island redoubt —the smaller of the two Marin islands off San Rafael. But even there they are not secure and on occasion have been easy prey for teen-agers with shotguns. Fortunately the birds inhabit the island in such great numbers that the illegal raids have not as yet made serious inroads on their population.

Of the eight varieties of sea gulls which can be seen over the bay—following fishing boats in droves, cleaning the beaches of refuse, nesting on rocks and on girders of the Bay Bridge—the only permanent resident is the Western gull, a large white bird with gray back and wings. The other species stay in this region during the winter only, roosting by the thousands on the roofs of piers, and take off in the spring for distant parts, some for areas farther north along the coast, some for lakes in the Sierra, some for such an inland spa as the Great Salt Lake. Probably some of the bay's gulls were among those which saved the Mormon crops from grasshoppers a century ago and were immortalized by a monument in Salt Lake City.

The bay's diminishing marshlands are way stations for dozens of other varieties of shore birds who stop here on their twice-a-year migrations. Bay Farm Island, just south of Alameda, has long been one of the great bird resorts of the West, populated in season by many varieties of sandpipers, avocets, willets, godwits, plovers, killdeer, curlews, and many others. Occasionally bird enthusiasts are thrilled by catching a glimpse of rarer species such as Wilson's snipe or the phalarope, a small sandpiper-like bird with an odd habit of spinning like a top as it sits on the water.

Great flocks of ducks winter here, too—mallards, pintails, canvasbacks and half-a-dozen other varieties which come south from the lakes and bays of Canada and Alaska to spend the winter in the bay's more hospitable climate. Sometimes, however, their welcome is less hospitable than the weather; around the shallow edges of the bay are scores of sheds and duck blinds which in season hide hunters looking forward to a wild-duck dinner.

The long-distance champion of the migrants is the arctic tern, a bird which resembles a sea gull in appearance but flies with rapid wingbeats, hovering in one spot over the water like a hummingbird, then diving quickly to snare a fish. He does not linger around the bay, however, stopping only for a bite to eat on his semi-annual trip from pole to pole.

Even more spectacular as a diver, because of his greater size, is the big brown pelican, a year-round resident who soars over the bay scarcely batting a wing until his keen eyes detect a possible meal just beneath the surface. Then he suddenly plummets to the water, hits with a mighty splash, and snags his fish.

Although the bird is a fast diver, he is a slow swallower, a weakness exploited by the sea gulls. Often a single pelican will be closely followed by two or three gulls, competing with each other to snatch the big bird's meal from his long beak before he can manage to gulp it down.

One of the most rewarding sights to be seen over the bay is the visit of a flock of great white pelicans from their homes on the lakes of the Great Basin, east of the Sierra. Unlike the resident brown pelicans, they visit the bay only rarely, usually in the spring or fall. They are among the largest flying birds on earth, with a wingspread sometimes reaching ten feet.

A flight of seventy or eighty may appear off the Embarcadero, soaring high above the surface like a squadron of heavy bombers in line, scarcely moving a wing. They fly with impressive dignity, their long necks curved easily back, yellow bills resting forward, white wings glinting in the sun. Effortlessly they ride the air currents, with no apparent purpose or desire other than sheer enjoyment of the sunshine and the blue bay, unperturbed by the traffic along the shore or the boats below them. Even an occasional low-flying plane leaves them unruffled; they magnificently ignore the noisy mechanical intruder, holding their rightful place with placid dignity.

After several minutes, suddenly and without apparent signal, they all begin to turn, some in large arcs, some in small, tightly banked circles, until the entire flock is slowly revolving like a wheel or a solar system around some invisible sun. For perhaps fifteen minutes the formation evolves through various sizes and shapes as individuals and groups within it create their own random patterns of curving flight.

Then, with a simultaneous singleness of purpose, the wheeling formation dissolves into a long, rolling V-shaped figure that gradually merges into a single line, and the entire group is off again, paralleling the bay shore. Each bird follows the one ahead in graceful rises and dips and swayings from side to side, like beads on a long, undulating string. An individual may vary from the formation in his own fashion, yet all unite in a marvelously harmonious whole, like a ballet whose members follow the rhythmic pattern but are free to improvise within its framework as they choose.

When the formation changes, however, the entire flock moves apparently at the same instant, as if governed by radio signals. Like many birds, the pelicans possess a cerebellum—the part of the brain governing co-ordination—which is in some ways more highly developed than that of the human being. What communications, imperceptible to humans, pass among them, guiding their maneuvers, is a mystery as yet unpenetrated by science.

In their superb grace and dignity, in the beauty and mystery of their smoothly co-ordinated flight these great birds seem to epitomize and climax the bay's evolving pageant of life. From the most primitive mollusks in the ooze of the bay bottom to these majestic dwellers of the sky, the life of the bay is a single, unfolding drama of creation, a galaxy of societies as varied and complex as the cities on the shores.

EBB

The big white buoy marking submerged Blossom Rock, off Telegraph Hill, trails a long line of foam toward the west, as if it were moving upstream leaving a wake. The tide is ebbing strongly, flowing past the buoy like a river.

The entire four-hundred-square-mile surface of the bay is sliding toward the Gate. In all the marshlands around the far shores, streams of salt water are draining swiftly bayward. At Alviso and Redwood City, in Corte Madera Slough, around the Napa River, and in a thousand winding channels of the delta the outward-flowing waters suck and gurgle in the ebb, and the reeds and tules and grasses bend pliantly toward the bay. Small fish head upstream against the current, and on thousands of acres of muddy marsh bottom now being laid bare by the receding waters, clouds of sea birds— gulls and avocets and terns and sandpipers—wheel and swoop

in hungry excitement, swarming across the flats in the wake
of the draining waters, probing the soft mud for succulent
clams, worms, and water snails made vulnerable by the falling tide.

Ships at anchor in mid-bay are swung around on their lines
by the ebbing current, sterns toward the Gate, bows pointed
into the oncoming flow. Pilots of docking liners carefully
watch the swirls and eddies and guide their ships into the
current in order not to be slammed against the wharves. The
captain of the ferry crossing from Oakland swings his chug-
ging paddle-wheeler in a long arc to the south against the
full force of the receding bay to avoid being swept out toward
the Gate.

Drawn by the fallen surface of the sea and the tug of the
moon, the bay will continue to ebb and shrink until finally
the tides reverse and it is filled again by the returning
rhythms of the flowing ocean.

8

The Harvests

The legendary wealth in the vaults of the sunken *Rio de Janeiro* is small change compared to some of the other treasures in the bay. These same waters hold, for example, some $150,000,000 in gold and $14,000,000 in silver.

Unlike the treasure of the *Rio,* there is no doubt that this fortune exists. But the problem of getting it out is about as complicated as raising the wrecked liner. So far no one has figured out a practical way to do either. All this gold and silver floats around in suspension in the waters of all the seas of the earth.

It is even conceivable that the bay waters are more highly gold-bearing than those of the ocean, owing to the gold content of the streams and rivers coming down from the Mother Lode. But there is no way of making such a measurement short of actually extracting the gold itself from the water—

a process which would be far more expensive than the value of the metal recovered.

There are other treasures in the bay's waters, however, and many of them can be recovered. Their annual harvest is worth more that all the bay's irrecoverable gold and silver. These waters contain nearly 300,000,000 tons of dissolved salt. Most of it—about three quarters—is sodium chloride, enough to salt the breakfast eggs of the entire population of the United States for approximately twelve hundred years. The other salts are magnesium chloride, magnesium sulphate, calcium sulphate, and potassium sulphate—all harvested from the bay and incorporated into scores of products that are part of the fabric of everyday living.

The Great Salt Farm   The part of the bay where the harvest of salts takes place is remote from the centers of population and unfamiliar even to most bay area residents. Go thirty miles southeast of the Ferry Building—away from the urban bay of ships and bridges—and you are in another world. This is a place of sky and water and little else—of sky hung in winter with sweeping cloud canopies that loop their misty fringes down over the tops of the far-off hills, of calm water laced by long low levees that wind sinuously into the distance until they disappear in the watery flatness.

Here the only sounds are the plaintive cries of circling gulls, the chirp of mud hens, the shrill call of a curlew as he swiftly skims the glassy surface. In the fall flocks of ducks pass overhead in ragged V formations against the gray sky, and the towers of power lines stride in single file across the bay like steel-limbed giants, each matched by its inverted image in the calm waters.

This area is only one step removed from the primitive swamp, and in the sloughs beyond the levees the marsh life still abounds as it has for thousands of years. The slick black head of a seal may break the smooth surface of the water for a moment, then disappear, leaving only ripples. Deep in the tules an apparent mass of mud five feet across may slowly come to life as a big bat ray and undulate off into the deeper ooze.

Unlike most of the places where man extracts wealth from nature, here he has made little change in the ancient landscape. He has put his levees around it and his power lines across it, but he has not tamed it. A sense of the primeval remains, owing perhaps to the fact that man's job here is not to conquer nature but to facilitate its work. For the process of extracting salt from bay water depends on the elemental forces over which man has little control—the sun, the soil, the tides, the rain, and the winds.

Nowhere else on earth are these elements—plus human ingenuity—combined in the exact proportions which make salt farming on this scale possible. Here is a long rainless season with a warm sun and moving air which evaporates the water rapidly from spring to early fall. Here are thousands of acres of sea-level marshland formed by silt carried down from the hills to the bay's edge and washed by the regular rhythm of the tides. The result is a layer of hard clay that provides the marshes with a watertight floor. Encircling these marshes by levees created the world's largest solar evaporation plant, operated by the Leslie Salt Company. The shallow ponds now cover about forty square miles, nearly 10 per cent of the bay's surface.

Like the earth rhythms which govern the growing of crops on the land, the long cycle of seasonal changes in the tidal waters inevitably determines the natural chemistry which produces a salt crop in the bay. During the summer months practically no rain falls into the bay, and many of the streams which enter it diminish to a trickle or dry up entirely.

After months of steady evaporation the bay is at its saltiest; its saline content is close to that of the offshore ocean water. Then begins the "planting" phase of the cycle; at four points around the bay's southern shores workmen turn the big valves which open the flood gates at high tide and fill four irregularly shaped "concentrating" ponds, each several hundred acres in size and each the initial stage in a separate system of ponds.

For weeks the number-one ponds in each system are left undisturbed; the summer sun evaporates more of the water, leaving the minerals, increasing the salinity. When the salinity reaches the prescribed amount, the gates are opened and the brine flows by gravity into the number-two ponds— and so on throughout the system.

One such circulation system begins near Palo Alto; the brine is moved from pond to pond down the west side of the bay, crosses the mouths of creeks and sloughs through siphons, and continues to the vicinity of the Leslie refinery near Newark on the east shore. Total transit around the bay's end may take over a year. By that time the brine has passed through nine concentrating ponds; more than fifty inches of water have been evaporated from the surface of the pools.

From concentration-pond number nine, the "pickle" pond, the water is turned into a series of smaller rectangular crystallizing ponds. By then more than 90 per cent of the water which originally entered from the bay has been evaporated. The brine can hold no more sodium chloride in suspension; the white stuff begins to crystallize into a solid and sinks slowly to the bottom like an underwater snowfall, forming layers several inches thick. For every five gallons of bay water which entered the circulation system, there is one pound of crude salt on the bottoms of the pools.

The Autumn Race   Fly over the southern bay, particularly in spring and summer, and you see a spectacular sight:

the shore for miles is lined with the jigsaw-patterned pools in brilliant hues—greens, blues, purples, reds, pinks. These are the colors not of the water but of the algae, diminutive plants of many varieties which thrive in varying concentrations of brine. Green algae will grow most prolifically in relatively weak brine; red algae in brine of greater salinity.

The algae are regarded as a delectable dish by a little animal called the brine shrimp, which swims around in the salt-laden water. As the shrimp consumes the algae, the color of the ponds returns to normal. He is netted up out of the concentration ponds and in turn makes a succulent meal for tropical fish, among others those inhabiting Steinhart Aquarium in Golden Gate Park.

For nine months human activity in the salt pools consists mostly of letting nature take its course, of turning valves, maintaining levees, and taking samples of the brine to measure its salinity.

Then, suddenly, as summer comes to a close, the ponds spring to life. Now begins a race between man and the elements. After many months of warm sun and high evaporation, the water in the pools is at its saltiest point. Now, before the winter rains come in force to dilute the brine again, it is time for the harvest. Hundreds of seasonal workers come to the pools and quickly go into action. They drain the crystallizing ponds and expose the bottom—white with a thick crust of salt.

There are new sounds over the vast flatness of the salt beds; above the cries of the sea birds comes a harsh mechanical clatter. Out across the white bottoms of the drained ponds come the "bull crews" with tractors, crunching the salt like hard snow under the wheels. On top of the salt they lay narrow portable tracks. Then come the miniature trains—each consisting of twelve small gondola cars pulled by a gasoline engine—about the size of a children's train in an amusement park.

Alongside the railroad tracks two men operate a big machine roughly resembling a wheat harvester on a caterpillar tread. It sends revolving teeth into the salt crust, breaks it up into chunks about an inch in diameter, and loads it onto the trains in a continuous flow—four thousand pounds of crude salt every minute of the day.

Most of the men who run the tractors, the trains, and the harvesters come from the surrounding countryside for the three-month operation. One may be a farm hand from the hay fields; one a blacksmith in a forge; another a barber in a nearby small town. A few are college students; some are part-time clergymen; and one recent harvesttime worker was an M.D. from a foreign country, earning money to start a local practice. They come to the wet pool beds in rubber boots and warm clothing, prepared to work through their eight-hour shifts despite the weather. The operation continues around the clock into December, beneath floodlights at night, often under threatening skies, sometimes in pouring rain.

Several hundred yards away, floodlighted at night, is a white pile of crude salt big enough to fill a football stadium. There the trains are dumping their load; bulldozers crawl over the pile like insects on an anthill, distributing the white stuff evenly, raking it to the chutes where it is drawn off into the refinery or into railroad cars. There are several such salt piles around the bay, including one at Redwood City, where the salt is loaded directly into ships. The piles soon develop a firm crust, and rain has little effect on them.

They resemble nothing so much as smooth hills covered by snow—a fact profitably exploited by Hollywood producers. Swing-shift workers arriving at the plant have on occasion been startled by the spectacle of shapely starlets frolicking in the drifts and skiers energetically slaloming down the steep salt slopes—all for the grinding cameras.

In the refinery the crude salt is washed, dried, and put through a score of processes which vary according to the final destination. A surprisingly small proportion of the product—only 4 per cent—is destined for the home salt shaker. About half of Leslie's million tons a year is sent to chemical plants throughout the nation for use in dozens of products. The rest goes into salt blocks for cattle on ranges all over the West; into food-processing plants, where it is used as a preservative for meat, vegetables, and fruit; into tanneries, bakeries, lumber mills, and cheese plants. It is also used, oddly enough, in drilling oil wells, icing railroad cars, and de-icing highways.

The Chemical Crop   All this is the latest phase of a development which began a century ago when natural salt lay eight inches thick around the edge of the marshes and at low tide was available for the taking. Enterprising businessmen soon scooped up most of it to sell to gold hunters. Later they built some primitive salt works, damming lagoons, pumping the water by windmills that turned the south bay into a miniature Holland. A few of the windmills remain, flailing uselessly in the breeze, as evidence of that earlier era.

In 1901 a dozen small plants combined into the Leslie Salt Company, and the windmills and crude methods of the early days gradually gave way to more efficient electric pumps and modern techniques. The Leslie operation expanded until it included forty thousand acres of ponds, five bulk plants, and five hundred employees at peak season. It now supplies 80 per cent of the crude salt used in the West.

But salt refining is only the beginning of what happens to bay water when it is harvested. The main Leslie plant at

Newark is the first stage of a complex industrial pipe line. Some of Leslie's crude salt goes into the adjacent Morton refinery for similar processing. Bittern, the brine that is pumped off the crystallization ponds after the salt has settled, is still rich in other minerals and is piped to the nearby Westvaco Chemical plant, a ten-acre maze of pipe lines, boilers, tanks, and chemical aromas. There the bay water is further taken apart and converted into chemicals sold for a hundred uses, from insecticides to soil conditioners. Magnesias coming out of the Westvaco plant are transported in turn to the Lavino Company's factory next door, where they are used in making the kind of bricks that line steel furnaces.

Across the bay in South San Francisco is the Marine Magnesium Products Company, the first plant in the world to extract magnesium commercially from sea water. Among scores of other uses some of the magnesium produced here goes to the salt refineries; there it is used to coat the table salt and keep it flowing freely, enabling the advertising department to promise customers that the salt will pour regardless of the weather.

Thus is the bay harvested for its mineral content, and bay water originally taken in through the Leslie ponds or the Marine Magnesium intake pipe turns up eventually in an incredible array of products. Any resident of the West may make indirect use of bay water in dozens of household items. Chemicals from the bay may be used in the manufacture of the toothpaste he brushes his teeth with in the morning, the milk of magnesia he swallows for his health, the linoleum he treads on in his kitchen while preparing breakfast, the coils of his electric stove, the syrup he spreads on his hotcakes, or the salt he shakes on his eggs. They may even have enriched the soil which grew the wheat in the bread he toasts.

Bay products may also turn up in the making of the steel of the car he drives to work and the white side-wall tires it runs on, in the pump hose in the service station where he fuels up, and in the gasoline that powers the engine.

Substances that originally floated in the tidal currents under the Golden Gate Bridge and helped to buoy up the ships that sail the bay's surface may have been used in making the paint on his office walls, the ash tray on his desk, the fluorescent lights which illuminate the room, the paper he uses to write letters, the steak he eats for dinner, the glue which holds together the book he reads at night, the ink on its pages and the treads of the stairs he climbs to go to bed.

Oyster Pirates and Portland Cement   Although the mineral harvests, taken together, are the greatest single source of wealth from the bay, there are other harvests nearly as productive. These waters abound with animal life and its remains, reaped in a dozen different ways by men with dredges, nets, and traps.

Possibly one hundred thousand years ago the bay was discovered by the oysters. The first oyster larva one day was swept by the tides in through the Golden Gate, attached himself to a rock, and found he liked it there. His descendants grew on rocks and on each other, formed big reefs, particularly on the broad shallow bottom in the south, and proliferated for the next thousand centuries or so.

The California Indians found them choice eating, and the natives' shell mounds are largely the remains of oysters and mussels. White men, too, soon learned that the little shellfish made good food. In the early 1870s someone tried the experiment of transplanting into the bay some Eastern oysters, which are larger and even more tasty. They proved popular, and for fifty years in many of the shallow areas around the bay shore, particularly south of San Francisco to Palo Alto and in Richardson Bay, there were dozens of board-fence enclosures protecting the oyster beds from hungry skates, star-fish, and other predators.

There was no such protection, however, from the human variety. "Oyster pirates" prowled the bay in small boats and helped themselves from the private beds, particularly in foggy weather. They would sail to the beds as the tide was ebbing, wait for low water, which left the oyster shoals exposed, then walk across the beds, picking and sacking the oysters rapidly before the tide returned.

In a semi-fictional adventure story called "A Raid on the Oyster Pirates," Jack London described a coup he once scored while stalking the poachers for the "fish patrol." He and a companion pretended to join a pirate band operating in the south bay; as the thieves began picking farther away from their anchored sloops, London and his colleague tied the boats together and towed them off, leaving the poachers stranded. As the tide rose to their necks, the pirates were glad to be "rescued" by police boats.

In the early 1920s something went wrong with the bay's oysters. They began to have an unpleasant taste and grew very slowly or not at all. Apparently the waters of the bay were becoming too polluted with the wastes of the harbors and the growing cities on its shores to continue to produce good oysters in commercial quantities. Other places on the California coast, such as Tomales and Drake's bays, replaced San Francisco Bay as oyster producers; the beds and the plants here were abandoned, although remains of many of them are still visible in the shallow offshore areas.

Most of the imported Eastern oysters have died out, but the small native variety still grows in some quantities. Week-end oyster hunters wade out around the rocks at low tide, at places like Coyote Point near San Mateo and McNear's Beach in Marin, and pry off the little animals. Properly cooked, they are palatable and safe, but inexperienced chefs run the risk of typhoid.

At about the same time that the commercial beds were abandoned, a new use for oysters was found. During the geologic ages that oysters had been growing and dying in the bay, each little animal had left something behind him—a hard, durable shell, rich in lime. The shells accumulated until they formed layers in some places as deep as thirty feet. Someone discovered that he could scoop up great quantities of these shells from the bay bottom and use them to make cement. From that discovery a new industry was born.

Out in the middle of the bay east of San Mateo a big dredge thrusts its egg-beater snout into the bay floor and inhales great draughts of mud, water, and oyster shells, which it spews out continuously through a sixteen-inch pipe into steel barges moored alongside. Tugs tow the barges some ten miles to the Ideal Cement Company plant at Redwood City, where the lime-bearing shells and bay mud are used in almost exactly their natural proportion as a base for Portland cement. The bay is one of the few places in the world where cement is made from shells and possibly the only place where the shells and the mud exist naturally in almost exactly the right proportions for cement making.

For more than a quarter of a century this plant has been fed by the remains of the bay's ancient oyster population, and it is estimated that the bay floor is covered with enough shells to continue the operation another fifty years.

In the same lower bay area a dredge belonging to the Pioneer Shell Company performs a similar job in the oyster beds; its shells are washed free of mud and most of them hauled up the bay to Petaluma, the chicken capital of California, where they are ground up and used in poultry and cattle feed to supply the needed calcium. The durable qualities of the shell which protected the oyster are incorporated into the shell produced by the chicken. Bay area residents who find that their breakfast eggs do not crack in boiling water may owe their thanks to an oyster who lived on the bay bottom five hundred centuries ago.

Shrimp Boats   At about the same time that the first oyster was washed in through the Gate, a little crustacean about the size of a man's finger also entered the bay. It was the ancestor of the present bay shrimp, a slightly higher form of life than the oyster, not stationary but able to crawl for short distances along the bottom on long spidery legs or burrow down snugly into the muddy ooze. Its main form of transportation, however, was to drift on the tidal currents. So hospitable was the new environment that the shrimps soon became one of the most abundant forms of life in the bay. Over the millenniums they evolved into a distinct species, the *Crago franciscorum*, unique to the bay, tiny, tasty, and beloved of gourmets throughout the country.

They were first hauled up from the bay bottom not long after the Gold Rush by Italian fishermen using dragnets. About 1870, according to legend, an incident occurred that had a drastic effect on shrimp fishing in the bay. An unemployed Chinese cook begged a handful of shrimp from an Italian fisherman near Hunters Point. He cooked his meal over a driftwood fire, took one bite, and was so startled by the delicious taste that he raced to San Francisco's Chinatown and showed the delicacy to the head of his tong.

The tong chief knew a good thing when he saw it. He thought of the thousands of unemployed Chinese who had been imported for the building of the Central Pacific Railroad across the Sierra, had spent some time in the diggings of the Mother Lode, and had drifted down to the city when the gold ran out. He immediately sent to China for a supply of nets and a few experienced fishermen.

His business instinct paid off. Within five years fifteen hundred Chinese were engaged in the shrimp industry around the bay, fishing, shelling, cooking, drying, and selling the little crustaceans. By the end of the century there were twenty-six shrimp camps around the bay's shores, each headquarters for a fleet of shrimp boats. Dried shrimps were exported and fresh ones sold in San Francisco, where several restaurants always served a plateful of them for the customer to nibble while looking over the menu.

Although the Chinese shrimp camps have now dwindled to two or three, the fishermen still employ many of the same methods that were imported by their countrymen. Their triangular hand-woven trap nets, staked to the bottom to intercept the shrimps moving on the tide, are used no place else outside the Orient.

Anti-Chinese sentiment ran high in California as late as the turn of the century and resulted in various legal restrictions on the Chinese shrimp fishery. Although most of the curbs were subsequently removed, the law still limits the use of the Oriental trap nets to the area south of the Ferry Building. The result is the division of the bay's shrimp industry between the fishermen of Chinese ancestry in the south bay, based at Hunters Point, and those of Italian descent sailing from small ports around the northern shores.

Fisherman's Wharf   At San Francisco's Fisherman's Wharf the legends are young. They are not yet diluted by generations of retelling but are often related by eyewitnesses, for the life span of the Wharf coincides with that of many of its inhabitants.

To hear the legends of the Wharf, go out behind the big restaurants, the souvenir shops, and the tourist zone where the crab pots boil on the sidewalks and the pitch men for the cafés sing out the merits of the respective cuisines. Go out to the weather-beaten piers where the little crab boats are moored close together and old men kneel in the sun repairing their nets or stand along the railings talking animatedly in that curious Fisherman's Wharf blend of Italian and English. Stop in at the lunch counters where the fishermen eat; linger in front of the bait shops and marine supply stores and listen to the old-timers.

They'll tell you of the days when Tom DiMaggio's young son Joe was regarded as a ne'er-do-well because he'd rather play baseball in the sand lot behind the Wharf than go to work fishing with his father. And they'll tell you of the times he used to knock the ball out of the lot and break the windows of the streetcars passing down Stockton Street.

They'll tell you about the early days around the turn of the century when the crab boats were powered by lateen sails in the wind—or by oars and back muscles when the wind failed. Those were the days before the laws restricted fishing inside the Gate, and you could stand on the old sea wall with a hand net and scoop up the sardines by the bucketful.

You'll hear about the great days of the Wharf, not so long ago, when the sardines ran in schools of countless millions along the coast, when there were some forty sardine canneries and reduction plants going full blast around the bay, when the big sixteen-man purse seiners were moored so thick between the piers that you could walk from one pier to the other by climbing across their decks.

They used to go out the Gate at night in the dark of the moon, and suddenly, a few miles offshore, the water just below the surface would turn white, ablaze with the phosphorescence stirred up by millions of sardines. The nets would be lowered and come up alive with the squirming silver bodies of tons of the fish.

Then, in the late 1940s, the sardine catch dropped to almost nothing. Fishermen pulled up empty nets, shook their heads in puzzlement. After several disastrous seasons the purse seiners left the Wharf. State and federal governments spent millions of dollars investigating the great sardine disappearance, but no one yet knows the answer for sure.

Along the Wharf you can take your choice of the theories. There are those who will knowingly nod and say the atom-bomb tests at Bikini were responsible. Scientists talk about changes in the alkalinity of the water and resulting alterations in the quantities of the organisms that constitute the sardines' food supply. Some people say that the sardines were fished out by the increasing number of boats and the unlimited catches.

The most intriguing theory of all is that the sardines just got wise to the fishermen and sounded—went off into the deep water beyond the continental shelf to hide out. And one of these days, the theory goes, after enough sardine generations have passed, they'll forget what happened and come back to the coast. And then you'll see the greatest sardine run in history. It could happen next year, or even this year. Or maybe even tonight some lone fisherman going to his crab traps out beyond the heads will suddenly see the ocean light up like the Fourth of July . . . and the great days will return to the Wharf.

The Champion   Meanwhile, the little crab boats, two hundred strong, will continue to be the mainstay of the Wharf. The crab fleet has its legends too. There are legends of great fishermen like Tony Scafani and old Carlo Gelardi and Lorenzo Maniscalco, the "King of the Crab Fishermen." "Lawrence"—he insists on the anglicized name—is a stocky, barrel-chested man with a granitic, weather-hewn face. He carries a watch fob presented to him by his fellow fishermen inscribed: *"Al Campione"*—To the Champion.

He came from Sicily as a young man—as did most members

of the older generation along the Wharf—is well into his seventies and the head of a great family of twelve children and more than twice as many grandchildren. One of his sons is a doctor, another a priest.

Universally regarded as the bravest man on the Wharf, he pilots his little white *San Cristoforo* out the Gate in weather that keeps most other craft moored safely at the dock. Sometimes his is the only boat out the Gate. He sets his ring nets along the beach nearer the line of the breakers than any other fisherman dares to venture. And for nearly half a century he has consistently returned to the Wharf with the biggest crab catch in the fleet.

Such daring exacts its toll. Twice mountainous breakers have smashed into Maniscalco's boat and rolled it over. The second time another fisherman saw the accident, panicked, and headed full speed for the safety of the Wharf. Then he thought better of his frightened retreat and chugged back out to the scene of the capsizing. Maniscalco was still clinging to his overturned boat, drenched and cold. But he refused to get aboard the rescue craft until its skipper would put a line on the *San Cristoforo* and tow it in. The rescuer, fearing for the safety of his own boat in the breakers, declined to do so. The two fishermen shouted Italian imprecations at each other over the roar of the surf until Maniscalco turned numb in the icy waters and almost lost his hold, then was dragged into the rescue boat, still protesting. The *San Cristoforo* was smashed in the breakers. But the Campione bought a new *San Cristoforo* from his savings and soon was again hauling up crabs barely outside the line of the breakers.

Like many of his fellow fishermen along the Wharf, Maniscalco invested his earnings, bought a big house in the Marina District, and probably commands more wealth than most of the well-dressed tourists who stare out the restaurant windows at the hard-working, overall-clad fishermen.

Crab fishing is best in the first few weeks after the opening of the season in November. By spring the catch has dwindled considerably, and about half the Wharf's fishermen secure their boats, stack their traps, and prepare for the annual spring migration—the air-lift to Alaska.

Generations of fishermen have made the trek to the north for the Alaska salmon, first individually in their own boats on the long dangerous haul for more than two thousand miles up the coast, then together on big windjammers like the *Balclutha* (now anchored as a showpiece near the Wharf), then on steamboats, and in recent years by plane. The trip is subsidized by the Alaska packers, who import fishermen by the thousands from all the coastal ports to take advantage of the few weeks of the great Alaskan salmon runs.

Then at the end of July the migrant fishermen return from Alaska to the Wharf, get out their boats, and join their colleagues who stayed behind, trolling for local salmon out around the Farallones.

The boat population of the Wharf is almost doubled in summer when the big albacore boats, based in other ports, come in to unload their catches. The big silver-blue tuna are caught mostly by troll lines far off the coast, from one hundred to two hundred miles out.

Not all the fishing craft permanently based at the Wharf are crab boats; about forty are trawlers or drag boats, twice as big as the crab boats. They are operated by a crew of several men, and most of them are owned by the fish wholesalers. They pull their long dragnets along the bottom as far out as the edge of the continental shelf, forty miles offshore, hauling up the bottom fish—sole, rock cod, sand dabs, flounders, and usually some crabs.

Often when the crab catch is poor, some of the fishermen drop their gill nets around Angel Island or San Pablo Strait and haul in smelt or herring, which enter the bay to spawn.

Or in the summertime they go up through Carquinez to Suisun Bay, the only place where they can legally use their gill nets to catch salmon. There they join the fishermen from Pittsburg, who confine most of their fishing to the Suisun and delta areas.

The Passing of an Era   The story of Fisherman's Wharf began in 1900, when the state set aside the waterfront between the foot of Taylor and Leavenworth streets for commercial fishing boats. Previous docks for commercial boats had been at the foot of Vallejo and the foot of Union, but as bay shipping expanded, the fishermen were moved out of the busiest area to the present location.

From the beginning fishermen sold parts of their catch to housewives, directly from their sailing craft, and some of them set up stalls on the piers and developed a regular market. Then one enterprising fisherman had the idea of selling clam chowder across his counter to hungry patrons. Fisherman Tom Castagnola expanded the practice; he put in some benches and tables and developed the crab cocktail, a small portion of crab meat with a special sauce. Shrimp cocktail also proved a popular dish, especially during prohibition, when other kinds of cocktails were slightly more difficult to come by. He tried mixing crab with Thousand Island dressing and developed the "crab Louie," which in time became the Wharf's most popular dish.

Castagnola soon found it more profitable to sell his boat, buy his fish from other fishermen, and devote his full time to the store. Others did the same. The late Mike Geraldi, for example, abandoned a twenty-six-year fishing career, built a restaurant—Fisherman's Grotto—took his sons into the business, and served the first complete sea-food meals on the Wharf.

Several Wharf families also opened restaurants—the Aliotos, the Sabellas, the DiMaggios. The first break in the solidly Italian tradition came when two businessmen named Gene McAteer and Bill Sweeney opened a restaurant in 1946 and, self-conscious about their names, labeled it "Tarantino's."

The old era on the Wharf is passing. Fathers who once fished the Mediterranean and still speak in the accents of Southern Italy are being succeeded by sons who learned jive talk at Galileo High, served their time in the armed forces, and would rather watch television than play an accordion and sing of old Sorrento.

The Wharf is gradually growing less clannish; the days are gone when the entire fleet, loaded with fishermen and their big families, would sail on a Sunday to some wooded Marin shore for a mass picnic. Many of the boats are still painted blue and white, the colors of the fishermen's patron saint, La Madonna del Lume, but the only community custom which remains is the annual blessing of the fleet. On the first Sunday of October a long procession winds down from Sts. Peter and Paul's Church to the Wharf, where each boat is given the blessing by the priest.

Fishermen like Maniscalco are a vanishing tribe—a rugged breed of men who earn their living by working alone against the elements with little more than some basic equipment and their own skill and muscle. The one-man boats are giving way to larger craft worked by a crew. The old-timer who could look over the side in a fog, watch the waves' angle of impact, and tell his location is being replaced by the younger navigator who knows how to use an electronic depth finder, charts, and direction finders. The fisherman who is alone all day with his thoughts on the rolling ocean is giving way to the youngster who likes to chat with other fishermen over his two-way radio, contact the marine operator and phone his girl friend or tune in on the local disk jockeys.

But crab fishing is not yet a safe or easy occupation. The fishermen still have to face storms and fogs and cold and rain. They still go to work in the middle of the night, and their boats move out the Gate before dawn in a long parade, the lights flickering across the dark surface of the bay like the beacons of some phantom fleet. The bay and its offshore approaches are their life and livelihood and will continue to be, as long as crabs can be hauled from the ocean floor and the leaping silver salmon rise to the bait.

COLORS

When an overcast breaks up, the coming of sunlight to the waters is like the coming of spring to the land.

At first, as the sun begins dimly to penetrate the cloud cover, vague, lambent lights play at random on the surface, an anticipation and promise of what is to come. At widely scattered areas the gray surface is touched with an almost imperceptible hint of misty green, like the first faint grass on the hills at the end of winter.

As a small section of the cloud ceiling thins and dissolves into pure sunlight, the water beneath it is slowly suffused with color—gray-green turning through several successive shades to brilliant aquamarine. Slowly the ceiling breaks up into billows of cumulus, flying low over the bay like flocks of woolly sheep, casting moving patterns of light and shade and color across the waters.

The sun, warming the air over the water, stirs up a breeze; and the breeze scuffs up small swells. Toward the sun the light shines through their translucent tops, touching them with emerald fire. Away from the sun the light is reflected from the opaque backs of the waves, and their color is a changing series of blues, from a smoky near-gray to deep cobalt.

Shafts of sunlight play across the surface like searchlights from above. The clouds cross the bay and pile up against the eastern mountains, leaving the land below them in shadow. Slowly entire cities appear out of darkness and disappear again; hills and mountains loom against a leaden backdrop, then are gone, swallowed up in the maw of a cloud. Islands are spotlighted in the sun, then in a moment turn dark against a glowing bay. Boats creep over the surface like water insects, crossing dazzling zones of greens and browns and blues.

At length the clouds, driven by the wind, surmount the eastern hills and disappear, and an incandescent brilliance wells up from the entire bay, as if from a fountain of light.

9

Shipwrecks

On quiet days in spring and early autumn when the bay is a placid pool with scarcely a ripple, and its glassy surface benignly reflects the mild sky, it is difficult to believe that this serene natural harbor can be on occasion one of the most hazardous of the world's major ports. Yet along the bay's rocky beaches and on its floor lies the wreckage of vessels of all sizes, and scores of human beings have met death in its waters—victims of fogs, treacherous currents, reefs, and human errors.

Although in recent years loss of life has been remarkably low, the annals of the bay in the century since it has been a large port contain records of several major disasters and at least one genuine legend.

The Rio de Janeiro   The steamer *City of Rio de Janeiro,* bound for San Francisco from the Orient, was two days behind schedule. All the way across the Pacific she had fought head winds and high seas, and it was with special anticipation that her passengers peered beyond the ship's bow on the morning of February 21, 1901. They were rewarded at midmorning when the *Rio* hove into sight of the mainland—a thin line of blue on the horizon.

Then just before noon came the first of a series of mishaps. Four miles off the Cliff House the ship nosed into a fog so thick that her skipper was forced to drop anchor and wait for clear weather.

All afternoon the Pacific Mail Steamship Company vessel, with 211 people on board, rode the offshore swell, enveloped in a gray world of its own, while her master, Captain William Ward, impatiently paced the bridge. There was no sound but the creaking of the anchor chains and the persistent clang of the ship's fog bell, which was rung every thirty seconds as a warning to other vessels that might be in the vicinity. No other ship came near, however, and for all the passengers could see or hear they might as well have been anchored in mid-ocean.

The dead monotony of waiting was broken late in the afternoon when the tiny pilot boat, attracted by the sound of the bell, appeared out of the fog. A rope ladder was lowered and pilot Fred W. Jordan clambered up, carrying under his arm a very welcome bundle—the late San Francisco newspapers.

The papers seemed a good omen—tangible reassurance that the sight of the mainland that morning had not been an illusion. One passenger excitedly riffled through the back sections of the papers until he found the item he had been looking for: He had just become the father of a son. Other passengers had their own special reasons for wanting to get ashore. Rounseville Wildman, U. S. Consul General at Hong Kong, accompanied by his wife and young son, was anxious to get into the city in time to catch a train for Washington and attend the inauguration of President McKinley. And it is likely that thirty-eight-year-old Captain Ward himself was in a hurry to get into harbor to greet his fiancée, a San Francisco girl.

Early in the evening it looked as if the long wait were over. The fog seemed to thin out, and the captain ordered the crew to haul up the anchor. Slowly the *Rio* probed toward the Golden Gate. But before she had gone far, the fog closed in again. Captain Ward disgustedly retired to his cabin, leaving word to be awakened if the fog lifted.

Shortly after 4:00 A.M. Jordan, the pilot, his eyes weary from staring into the fog, thought he spotted a clear space. As he blinked shoreward into the blackness, he saw lights glimmering at regular intervals. From his years of experience he knew they were the lighthouses at Point Bonita and Fort Point. He called the ship's master.

At 4:30 the engines of the *Rio* began to throb, and the ship cautiously moved into the channel at half speed, heading toward the center of the Gate. Thirty minutes later the vessel hit a patch of fog, then quickly broke through it. With most of her passengers still sleeping the ship passed Land's End and its small outpost of Mile Rock. The Point Bonita light moved slowly along the portside until it was well astern.

Then suddenly, as the ship neared the narrows of the strait, another wall of fog loomed ahead.

The Fatal Decision   Before every great shipwreck there is a single crucial moment when an immediate and final decision must be made. Once that moment is passed, no further choice is possible. It was such a decision that the master of the *Rio* had to make shortly after 5:00 A.M. in the darkness of that winter morning.

The ship earlier had passed quickly through one patch of fog; quite possibly this was another like it and in a few seconds she would emerge into the clear. To stop in mid-channel would be to run the risk of collision with any other ship that might come nosing through the mists. An attempt to anchor here would be risky; charts showed that in this area the channel was deeper than at any other place inside the Farallones —forty to fifty fathoms, and at some points it exceeded sixty fathoms. The bedrock bottom, washed smooth by running tides, afforded little grip for the hooks. And the currents were swift; even now the ship was running against a powerful six-knot ebb tide.

All these considerations may have flashed through the captain's mind at that instant. He may have thought of the girl in San Francisco he planned to marry. He may have considered the sleeping passengers below and their disappointment if morning came and they were still not ashore. Whatever his state of mind, Captain Ward's decision was soon made; he decided to keep the ship on course. For nearly twenty minutes the *Rio* plowed cautiously through the fog.

At exactly 5:25 there was a grinding lurch that jarred the ship with the force of a powerful earthquake. The men on the bridge were thrown from their feet. The lights went out. Below decks, passengers were tossed from their beds. The bow rose high and the vessel listed sharply to port.

Unknown to the captain or pilot, the ship had been swept off course by the deadly "set toward Fort Point"—an erratic current moving southward toward the headland projecting into the Golden Gate at the narrows. The *Rio* had struck the Fort Point ledge, and sheer momentum carried her bow up onto the rocks.

The captain jumped to the deck to direct the lowering of the lifeboats. Crewmen ran to their posts, and frightened passengers scrambled across the listing deck to the rail.

Launching of the boats was hampered by the intense fog, so thick, one passenger later testified, that it was impossible to see a person at arm's length. Some of the passengers climbed down rope ladders into the boats. Hand lanterns glimmered in the dark. Captain Ward returned momentarily to the bridge and tied down the ship's whistle cord. The bellow of alarm echoed from the nearby cliffs.

Pilot Jordan found the seven-year-old son of Consul General Wildman.

"Lifting up the little boy," he said later, "I placed his arms around my neck and told him to hold fast and then started down the ladder. This was perhaps fifteen minutes after we struck. The steamer had already filled considerably and was listing strongly to port.

"When I was half-way down the ladder, everything seemed to drop downward and my hold on the ladder was broken. I must have been carried under at least fifty feet and was almost stunned. The little boy was wrenched from me and I never saw him again . . ."

A mile away at Baker's Beach an Italian fisherman burst excitedly into the lifesaving station and began talking so rapidly that Coast Guardsmen had to quiet him down before they could learn that he had seen a big ship sink. Quickly they sent word to other stations and launched their rescue boats. But, blinded by the fog, they were at a loss as to where to begin searching.

Soon the entire city was alerted. Fishermen and other boat-owners headed for the scene. Thousands of people went to the cliffs along the Gate and stood peering into the fog. All morning rescue boats and fishing craft picked up survivors. The *Rio's* lifeboats had been scattered all the way to Point Bonita.

Of the 211 people aboard the *Rio*, 131 went down with the ship, including Captain Ward and Consul General Wildman and his family. It was the greatest shipping disaster in the bay's history and the source of its most persistent legend.

The Treasure of the Golden Gate   Although wreckage littered the beach for months afterward, the hulk of the *Rio* disappeared, and divers probing the black waters at the bottom of the channel failed to find any trace of the vessel. The fog that surrounded the sinking of the ship was replaced by swirling mists of rumor and myth which thickened as the years went by. For more than half a century afterward the mystery of the vanished *Rio* stimulated the imaginations of seamen and landlubbers alike.

Along San Francisco's waterfront it was said that a fortune in gold bullion was in the hold of the ship, awaiting anyone who could salvage it from its stronghold at the bottom of the Gate. Ship's officers and officials of the Pacific Mail line stated after the wreck that the ship had carried $300,000 in opium, $400,000 in silk—and no gold. It was said that the officials had denied the existence of the gold to prevent treasure hunters from recovering it before it could be salvaged by the owners themselves. According to one theory, the gold was carried as registered mail and thus not listed in the ship's cargo.

The amount of the treasure aboard was at first rumored to be a quarter of a million, grew to two million, later to six. Whenever an unidentified piece of wreckage was found on the beach, the legend of the *Rio's* treasure was revived and expanded. Fifteen years after the wreck a water cask from the ship was discovered and provided occasion for one of the survivors to recall that the *Rio* had been sailing under a "curse."

In mid-Pacific, the story went, a crewman had broken into the stateroom of two girls but was apprehended before he could do any harm and placed in irons by the captain. For eighteen days he was chained to an iron stanchion on the main deck and fed only on bread and water. From morning to night he had cursed the ship and prayed that she would go down with all on board.

Another legend grew out of a discovery near Benicia in 1919 of fragments of wreckage which could have been parts of the *Rio*. How had the wreckage gotten to Benicia, inside Carquinez Strait some forty miles from the Gate? Someone surmised that maybe there was a tunnel beneath the bay bottom. One newspaper writer speculated: "Is the *Rio de Janeiro* now lying wedged in the entrance to some subterranean cavern whose mouth sucks from the waters of the Pacific and whose farther end terminates in the Carquinez straits?"

Writers continued for decades to advance theories on the complete disappearance of the *Rio*: It had been swept out to sea; it had been carried into the inner bay; it had berthed in a cave beneath Fort Point ledge; it had been sucked into a bottomless pit; it had been seized by a gigantic sea serpent. The theories in time became part of the legend.

Periodically, adventuresome divers continue to probe the bay bottom, looking for the ship and its treasure, finding nothing but setting off new waves of speculation. A mining engineer named Walter E. Plank laid claim to being the only living eyewitness to the sinking. He related that he had been a boy of sixteen living with his family near Fort Point on that February day in 1901. He was awakened by the sound of the ship's whistle, ran down the cliff to the beach, and saw through the fog the bow of the ship riding high in shallow water on the beach. He waded out to the vessel, saw no sign of life, failed in an attempt to climb aboard, and was hiking back up the hill when the ship slipped back into deep water and sank. The loss of life might have been averted, he theorized, if the passengers had jumped off the bow into shallow water instead of taking to the boats.

Another old-timer, retired postal inspector William Ives

Madeira, had an even more fascinating story. As assistant postmaster in Honolulu, the *Rio's* last port of call, he said that he had personally loaded on board the vessel on the night of February 15, 1901, $75,000 in gold coin in registered mail, sent by two Honolulu banks. As he placed the money, loaded in canvas bags, on the floor of the vault, he saw there several large stacks of metallic bricks that he thought at first were lead.

"What's that?" he asked the ship's purser.

The purser replied with an answer to send chills down the spine of all those who love tales of sunken treasure.

"Chinese silver," he said. "Two million dollars' worth."

It seems probable that the hulk of the *Rio* will never be found and her mystery will forever remain unsolved. And perhaps it is best that way. She is worth more as a legend. One would prefer to believe that the old ship still lies out there someplace on the bottom, her vault loaded with gold coin and encrusted bars of silver. . . .

Ships' Graveyard   Land's End, the sea-battered stretch of cliffs and rocks on the south shore of the Golden Gate just before it opens into the ocean, might well be called Ships' End. Walking for a mile along the cliffs from Phelan Beach to the Cliff House, you can look below and still view the remains of several vessels which have piled up in this maritime graveyard.

A few yards offshore, opposite the Mile Rock lighthouse, you can see protruding from the water at low tide two brown shapes which at first glance are indistinguishable from the jagged rocks which litter this beach. But, on closer inspection, they appear to be parts of badly rusted bulkheads or engine blocks. Nearby, closer to shore, is some smaller unidentifiable wreckage, including what seems to be a mast rising out of the water.

The story behind this wreckage is an odd one. These are the remains of two sister ships that met the same fate and share the same watery tomb. The *Lyman Stewart* was rammed by the freighter *Walter Luckenbach* in a dense fog in the Golden Gate in October 1922. The *Frank H. Buck* was struck by the liner *President Coolidge* in a dense fog in the Gate in March 1937. Both were tankers loaded with oil which spread across the surface of the water like blood from wounded whales. Both drifted several hours on outgoing currents before running aground near Mile Rock. Oil from the *Lyman Stewart* clogged the intakes of Sutro Baths on the ocean front a half mile away; oil from the *Frank H. Buck* soaked swimming sea gulls so hopelessly that they were unable to fly, forcing the S.P.C.A. to put them out of their misery. And the day after each accident the cliffs of Land's End were lined with picnicking San Franciscans eating hotdogs and gazing at the wreck.

All attempts to budge the tankers off the rocks failed. The *Lyman Stewart*, slightly closer to shore, was used as a shelter by down-and-out ex-sailors from Skid Row until the pounding waves made her uninhabitable. Both vessels were in time reduced to fragments by the pounding surf.

Scattered along the rocky beaches of Land's End are pieces of rusted steel from other vessels. One of them was the lumber steamer *Coos Bay*, which ran aground in a fog in 1927; members of the crew were evacuated by breeches buoy along a cable to the cliff top. Another was the grounded freighter *Ohioan*, wrecked in 1936; its boilers are still visible at low tide just north of the Cliff House.

The most spectacular wreck of all was undoubtedly that of the schooner *Parallel*, which ran aground in 1887 near the Cliff House with eighty thousand pounds of dynamite aboard.

The ship and, presumably, the Cliff House were evacuated in the nick of time. The explosion was heard for a hundred miles and took the north end of the Cliff House with it.

The Great Ferry Collision   The most renowned of the bay's sunken ships was probably the ferry *San Rafael*, which had the distinction of having been sunk once in real life and three times on the screens of the nation's movie houses. The original accident was used by Jack London as the basis for the opening sequence of *The Sea Wolf*, the novel that was made into three motion pictures.

Ironically, the sinking of the *San Rafael* occurred partly as a result of efforts to make the bay safer for navigation. In November of 1901 a dredge was anchored just west of Alcatraz while it was engaged in the removal of Arch Rock as a menace to navigators. To avoid the dredge in a heavy fog on Saturday night November 30, the ferry *Sausalito*, bound for San Francisco, followed a course east of Alcatraz instead of taking its normal course west of the island.

The skipper of the northbound *San Rafael*, aware that the *Sausalito* was due to be in that vicinity, was listening for its whistle while steering blindly around the island's east side. He heard it—but too late. Almost immediately the *Sausalito's* bow appeared through the fog. There was a quick, jarring impact and the sound of bending steel, splintering wood, and breaking glass.

The bow of the *Sausalito* had plowed directly into the crowded restaurant of the *San Rafael*, killing a cook and injuring many of the diners. The rest began a panicky rush for the exits. The boat began to list immediately. Doors were blocked by the crowds; seats and life preservers were used to smash windows for escape.

Alert crew members lashed the two ferries together, and

most of the passengers were able to climb directly across the ships' rails. Within twenty minutes the sinking *San Rafael* was evacuated, and as it settled lower in the water, threatening to drag the *Sausalito* with it, the lines were severed.

Meanwhile the two ships had drifted west on a strong ebb tide to a point about a mile inside the narrows of the Gate and there the *San Rafael* went to the bottom. The *Sausalito* limped into the San Francisco dock with her double load. Total fatalities aboard the *San Rafael* were four: the cook, two passengers, and one horse; the animal had balked at climbing the rail to the other ferry.

Although the sinking of the *San Rafael* was the bay's most famous ferry accident, it was not the worst. In terms of loss of life it was exceeded by the strange tragedy of the ferry *Peralta,* which took place on a calm, fogless day in 1928 when no other vessels were in the vicinity.

The *Peralta* was crowded with commuters on the 5:15 run to Oakland and was halfway between Yerba Buena and the Oakland pier when disaster struck so quickly that passengers were unable afterward to give any consistent accounts of what had happened.

Out of a clear sky and a calm bay a wave washed up over the open bow of the vessel with such force that more than twenty passengers were swept overboard. Others, believing the boat was sinking, jumped over the side. The ferry was undamaged and picked up most of the lost passengers, but five were drowned.

The probable cause of the accident was later brought out in the investigation. The *Peralta* was equipped with ballast tanks in which water could be shifted from one end of the boat to the other to compensate for the crowding of passengers at either end in loading and unloading. On this occasion, as the vessel approached Oakland and the passengers jammed together on the bow to unload, a confused crewman evidently shifted the water to the front instead of the rear, temporarily submerging the bow under the double weight of the ballast water and the passengers.

Although waves from ocean storms soon lose their force as they roll in through the Gate, the bay is capable of mounting good-sized storms of its own. A gale from north or south can whip up a sea high enough to swamp small craft. In November of 1945 a twenty-six-foot Navy boat carrying sailors to their ships was overturned by big waves between San Francisco and Alameda and eleven of its twenty-seven passengers were drowned.

But the tragedy was a minor occurrence compared with what was to happen just five years later.

The U.S.S. Benevolence   The skipper of the U.S.S. *Benevolence* had reason to be well pleased with his ship.

The 15,000-ton vessel was just completing a successful day-long series of tests outside the Golden Gate and was returning to harbor. Giant red crosses on each side of the gleaming white craft marked her as a hospital ship. She had just been "de-mothballed" and refitted at Mare Island Navy Yard for service in the Korean War, which had broken out just two months earlier. Below decks was $10,000,000 worth of shining new hospital equipment.

It was late on an August afternoon and the usual summer fog bank was hovering along the coast. The fog was not unusually thick; the ship would nose through a few wisps of it then emerge into the clear, with visibility of a half mile or more. As a routine measure the *Benevolence* sent out a fog signal—a single long blast every sixty seconds.

The last thing in the skipper's mind was the possibility of danger, and he scarcely slackened his speed as the ship entered the main channel six miles off Point Lobos. It had been a half century since the wreck of the *Rio* and thirteen years since a major ship collision had occurred in the bay. Since that time World War II had brought about a revolution in the science of navigation, making the clumsy, groping ships of the pre-war era seem primitive by comparison. Radar enabled navigators to penetrate the thickest fog and locate nearby vessels long before they could be spotted from the bridge.

The ship was heavily loaded, with 526 people aboard, including two crews—a fact which may have contributed to the confusion later. One was the Navy crew that had been operating the vessel in the few days since its de-mothballing. The other was the civilian crew scheduled to take over the job on a permanent basis.

There were three captains on the ship's bridge—the Navy skipper in command of the vessel, the civilian master scheduled to take command, and the civilian pilot, who took over navigation to guide the ship through the channel and into the bay.

At 4:50 P.M. the *Benevolence* was moving along the right-hand side of the channel at a fast fifteen-knot clip, plowing up a good-sized bow wave. Visibility had decreased and was at times less than a ship's length ahead. But the radar men kept close watch on their electronic screen as its sweeping hand clearly revealed the buoys marking the channel. They also saw five other ships within the scope's nine-mile radius— all at considerable distance. The vessels' positions were duly reported to the bridge.

Suddenly the pilot on the bridge tensed. "I hear a whistle," he said. "It's dead ahead."

He gave a rapid order which was passed on by bells to the engine room: full stop. The *Benevolence's* engines ceased their throbbing. The men on the bridge squinted into the fog, listening. They heard nothing.

What happened in the next two or three minutes was later disputed. The officers on the bridge said the engines remained stopped. But the engineer in charge said that after the first stop-engine order he received another command, "Ahead two thirds," and proceeded to put it into effect.

Whatever was occurring in the engine room, there was no argument as to what next took place on the bridge. The three captains heard another whistle—a single long blast, much louder than the first. Almost instantly they saw a sight that tightened knots in their stomachs. The black hull of a big freighter broke out of the fog several hundred yards dead ahead. The pilot shouted: "Right full rudder!"

Below in the mess hall members of the crew were noisily eating supper when they felt the ship swing sharply to starboard. They looked up curiously.

The men on the bridge watched in a cold sweat as the freighter seemed to knife on through the fog in a direct line for the *Benevolence*. It "came out of the fog," said the civilian captain later, "like something out of a cardboard box." The *Benevolence's* collision-alarm siren began to wail.

The hospital ship had turned about ten degrees to the right when the freighter struck. With an earsplitting grinding and ripping of metal the freighter's stem crumpled the steel plates of the *Benevolence's* port bow. The *Benevolence* rolled to starboard, and there was a second impact as she righted herself. Below in the mess hall the diners were sent sprawling across tables; crewmen standing on decks or in passageways were slammed against bulkheads.

Tragedy of Errors   The skipper had given an order over the public address system to stand by with life jackets and close the watertight doors. But of the nine crew members who had been assigned to man the doors only one was on duty at the time; the others were in the mess hall or the chow line.

The freighter had ripped a fifty-foot hole in the *Benevolence*, above and below the water line, then pulled back into the fog. The hospital ship quickly began to list to port as the water poured in.

The Navy captain in command was certain the ship would remain afloat; shortly after the collision he ordered a radio message sent to Navy headquarters: "Am four miles off Golden Gate Bridge and need emergency assistance. . . ."

Others were not so certain. As the *Benevolence* continued to list sharply, crew members headed for the lifeboats. But no one knew exactly where to go; there had never been a boat drill on board and the crew had not been given lifeboat stations.

The radio operator tapped out an SOS. But the message was never heard. He had forgotten to connect the radio's antenna, and the key was dead.

Crowds gathered around the lifeboats and frantically struggled to operate the mechanical releases. But the ship's power had failed. Then they tried to operate the hand cranks releasing the boats, but the ship was listing so badly they could not loosen the shackles. The boats were locked in position.

Only one of the ship's sixteen lifeboats was ever released. Fortunately some life rafts were loosened and thrown overboard.

Within five minutes after the collision the main deck was awash and the vessel continued to roll over. People began to go over the side by the dozen. Men struggled with each other for available life jackets as they went into the water. The chief medical officer rounded up the ship's dozen nurses, found some rope and tied them together. Then he found three boards.

"We slid the boards off the hull," one of the nurses said

later. "By this time the ship was completely on its side and we walked off the bottom of the ship into the water."

The girls clung to the boards in the icy sea. One became hysterical. Another began a grimly cheerful chorus of "Merrily We Roll Along."

Forty minutes after the collision the big white ship went under. The captain in command, who later admitted he never realized the vessel was going down until he was washed off into the ocean, had never given an order to abandon ship.

All the fatal mistakes were not made aboard the *Benevolence*. The master of the freighter, the *Mary Luckenbach,* had been proceeding at a fifteen-knot speed outward through the fogbound channel. His radar was out of commission, and there was some evidence later that the ship had been off course—and was in the inbound lane.

"At 4:58," the captain said later, "I heard a whistle and stopped my ship . . . then ordered the engines full astern . . . At 4:59 I sighted a bow wash dead ahead, just as the fog lifted a little . . . I gave orders for hard right and sounded the danger signal—four blasts . . . At 5:02 we collided."

At 5:10 the *Luckenbach* captain testified, he dropped anchor. The *Benevolence* had disappeared in the fog. "We heard no distress signal," he said, "so concluded that the damage to the hospital ship was all above the water line and that she was proceeding into port."

For an hour and a half the freighter stood at anchor without lowering lifeboats, without making any radio inquiries. The ship's radio had not picked up any word of the disaster although by that time the news was flooding the commercial wave lengths. The captain said he had no idea the *Benevolence* had sunk until about 6:30 when the *Luckenbach* crew heard voices from the water and a Coast Guard boat came alongside with survivors.

The Hero from Fisherman's Wharf   Fisherman John Napoli had been trolling off the Farallones all day in his thirty-four-foot boat, the *Flora*. He had a good catch—five hundred fifty pounds of gleaming silver salmon, lying in four big boxes on the deck.

He was on his way back to Fisherman's Wharf and was still several miles offshore when he noticed through the fog what he thought was a turtle in the water. A minute later he was surprised to see through the mist the big hull of the *Mary Luckenbach*, riding at anchor. Then a Coast Guard boat appeared and someone aboard shouted at him. He thought it was something about a man overboard. With a sinking feeling in his stomach he recalled what he had just seen.

He waved for the Coast Guard boat to follow him and swung the *Flora* around to the spot where he had seen the "turtle." It was a man. He was bleeding from cuts and nearly unconscious. Napoli hauled him aboard.

Then for a moment the fog lifted. The fisherman stared around him in horror at the scene of the wreck.

"God Almighty," he said afterward, "those heads bobbin' all around like seagulls sittin' on the water. My hair stand up."

Time was short. Before long the survivors would be scattered for miles through the fog.

Working rapidly, Napoli dragged more survivors over the rail of his boat. Most of them were blue and shivering, unable to speak or to pull themselves aboard.

"I have to make plenty room so they don't hurt the other guys when they flop down. So I throw the boxes of fish overboard."

When the boat was full, he took his human catch to the *Mary Luckenbach*. As the helpless survivors were transferred to the big ship in wire baskets, the *Flora* rose and fell on the swells and banged against the steel hull of the freighter until her rail buckled.

Then Napoli set out for more. Occasionally the fog lifted enough for him to see the starboard side of the *Benevolence*, just beneath the surface, her portside resting on the bottom. And he could see other craft of the rescue fleet—Coast Guard cutters, private yachts, other fishing boats which had raced to the scene from the bay after hearing radio reports of the sinking—a miniature Dunkirk armada.

The air was full of the sounds of disaster—the shouts of the boat crews, the beat of the engines, the pleading cries of the people still in the water.

"The noise was somethin' terrible. When I get to thinking about it in my sleep it jumps me outa bed and I'm done for the night. You hear five hundred people hollerin', you never get it outa your system."

He fished one of the nurses up over the side. "She was barefooted and purple from the cold, but she just climb up to the bow and sit there. She don't complain one bit, not even a word."

It was growing dark when the exhausted fisherman put his last batch of survivors on a tug. Altogether he had pulled fifty-four people from the water. He heard somebody say that it looked as if all survivors had been picked up. Then as the *Flora* began to plow homeward he heard some weak shouts.

There ahead were sixteen Navy men in the water, ". . . all huggin' each other like a rug . . . I get 'em to the boat but I just ain't got the strength left to pull 'em up. I stood there and cried. I couldn't help it. I bawl like a baby. I tole 'em, 'Take it easy. I get you saved somehow.'"

He tied the swimmers to the crumpled rail of the *Flora* like a human raft and towed them to another boat, where they were lifted aboard.

Owing to the work of the Coast Guard and volunteer rescuers like Napoli, 498 of the 526 people aboard the *Benevolence* were saved. Even so, the death toll of 28 made it the worst ship disaster in the bay since the sinking of the *Rio*.

Coast Guard investigators concluded that the skippers of both ships were guilty of negligence. The *Benevolence* captain was court-martialed and the *Mary Luckenbach* skipper deprived of his licenses. The failure of the *Benevolence's* radar to pick up the *Mary Luckenbach* remained a mystery. It was speculated that atmospheric conditions in the Golden Gate had created a dead spot on the radar screen.

For two years the *Benevolence* lay blocking part of the main channel. At low tide on a clear day she was visible from the Cliff House, her white hull with its big red cross awash, her lifeboat davits protruding from the water.

Engineers finally decided that the cost of raising her would be prohibitive and dynamited her hull sufficiently to clear the channel. The last resting place of the *Benevolence* is indicated on Coast and Geodetic Survey charts just two miles off the Cliff House. Alongside the fifty-foot depth mark is the single word: "wreck."

Aftermath   As a result of exposure and the strains of pulling survivors aboard the *Flora* fisherman Napoli was hospitalized. Owing to consequent spinal trouble he was unable to continue fishing and had to put the *Flora* up for sale. Reporter John Campbell Bruce, who had written Napoli's story for the San Francisco *Chronicle*, happened to phone him at home a couple of months after the disaster.

"I'm fine," said Napoli in answer to Bruce's query. "Everything comin' along fine . . . Tomorrow a man is buyin' my crab traps."

Bruce asked him why he was selling his traps.

"I gotta eat. My wife got a job, but that don't catch up with the bills."

"What about your fishing?" Bruce inquired.

"I can't stand standin' up. My back hurts. I got to lay down. And you can't make a livin' layin' down."

Bruce wrote the story of Napoli's misfortunes for the *Chronicle* and later for the *Reader's Digest*. The *Flora* had been so badly banged up on the steel hull of the *Mary Luckenbach* that it would cost $1000 to put her back in condition. Sympathetic readers donated more than enough to repair the boat; later Napoli received a check from the Secretary of the Navy for $4422 for his lost cargo and damage to the *Flora*. And he continued to receive letters from people who read about him.

"I didn't think so many people would . . . no foolin', I feel so happy about things . . . I feel very kind to those people."

The story of the hero of the *Benevolence* should have a happy ending. Unfortunately, the gifts and compensation could not make up for the loss of his livelihood due to the injuries he incurred. Deprived of his trade as a fisherman, he was able to eke out a living by taking whatever work he could get along the docks. Ruefully he recalled that, when he was in the hospital after the wreck, many of the people he had rescued, including the nurse and sixteen Navy men, had come to see him, and some had offered him large sums of money.

". . . They came to see me all together. I got so choke up I couldn't say hello, boys. Everybody's grateful and wants to pay me. One even offers $1000."

The fisherman had shrugged off the gifts.

"You save a fella's life, you don't take money for it. They do the same for you."

TEXTURES

Clouds hang low over the vast amphitheater of the bay and its shores like a pavilion roof supported by mountain pillars. The scene is a monochrome of grays of infinite shadings from silver to near-black. The morning air is still, and the bay is flat and glassy—a clean scroll ready to be written on by the winds, the fogs, the rain, and passing vessels.

A freighter leaves a spreading V-shaped wake of waves and ripples sharply etched on a surface of gun-metal gray. A tug crosses the ship's wake and sets up a conflicting series of wave lines which intersect those left by the freighter. A Coast Guard launch cuts across both wakes and adds its own trail to the patterns. The lines of swells left by each vessel continue to roll uninterruptedly across each other, spreading over constantly widening areas of the smooth surface, creat-

ing diverse curves, angles, crosshatches and herringbone corrugations in elaborately evolving geometric designs.

A breeze drifts in from the Gate, moving visibly across the water, ruffling the smooth surface, coming at first in arrow-like advance salients, then in billowing masses which soon cover the bay. The only area unaffected by the wind is a series of broad parallel streaks of smooth water, perhaps caused by films of oil left by passing vessels or washed from the shores. Rising tidal currents and passing boats weave the streaks into concentric arcs and interlacing curves which reflect sinuous tracings of light until the opaque surface is veined like fine marble.

The wind increases, gradually erases the patterns, and once again the bay is a uniform gray, now roughened and darkened by the shadows in the trough of each wave.

10

The Changing Shoreline

THE PLANS OF NATURE

In man's brief span of time on earth he regards the main features of his environment as permanent, much as one would glance at the single frame of a motion-picture film and fail to see any movement. But the processes which formed the bay, like those which created the earth and everything upon it, are unceasing, and man's glimpse of them in his lifetime reveals but a static interval in an endless continuum.

The sun, the rain, the wind, the ice, the rushing waters, and the moving sea are engaged in endless action and reaction, moving interminably in processes which not only seem to reach endlessly back into the past but also stretch far beyond man's dim vision into the future.

If the bay, and its shores, as we know them, are regarded not as a completed project but as some intermediate state in a long geologic evolution, what can be said of its future?

Geologists seldom make predictions. There are too many unforeseen factors that can enter the picture to confound the prophets. But the layman is free to indulge his imagination— to consider the clues and piece together a picture of what may happen.

Attack and Counterattack   As we have seen, the creation of the bay may be looked on as a series of conflicts between elemental geologic forces. The first conflict, between the ocean and the rising mountains of the Coast Range, was won by the mountains; and the ocean was rolled back nearly one hundred fifty miles. Then, in the struggle between the river and the mountains rising to block its course, the river was victorious and carved through the mountains the two gorges of Carquinez and the Golden Gate.

In the succeeding conflict between the river and the ocean the winner was the ocean, encroaching first on the river's delta, then invading and overwhelming its course for more than forty miles upstream to create the bay.

But the river has long been engaged in a massive counter-attack to reclaim its own—to push back the ocean and turn the bay into a valley once more. With the same powerful cutting action that enabled it to slice its way through the mountains, it continues to carve out its channel. Most of the material scooped from its bed and from thousands of miles of its tributaries—material it once deposited in the great delta outside the Gate—is now laid down in the bay itself.

Over the bay bottom the river has spread thick layers of mud, silt, and sand in some places three hundred feet deep. For example, the ridge which now supports the Bay Bridge, extending from the bridge's western anchor on Rincon Hill to Yerba Buena Island, has been buried under more than one hundred feet of mud. Measured by this standard, the bay is already more than half filled with sediment—halfway to being reconverted into a valley. In this effort to drive out the ocean, the river has small but potent allies. Around the edges of the bay, particularly on the Marin shore, where the hills rise steeply, there are canyons whose lower reaches were flooded by the advancing salt water as the ocean rose, creating what the geologists call "drowned valleys." Just as the bay itself was the drowned valley of the main river, so the arms of the bay extending back among the ridges are drowned valleys of tributary streams. These streams are themselves bringing down from the surrounding canyons great quantities of mud and silt, depositing them in the calm waters just offshore.

As the shore waters gradually become shallower, plants grow from the bottom, and the tidal marshes are created, intermediate stage between water and land; a marsh is a sign that the salt water is losing the struggle with the force of the streams. More sediment is deposited until it rises above sea level and becomes dry land.

As an illustration of how the streams are building their deltas and driving back the bay, drive north across the Golden Gate Bridge into Marin County. In the fifteen miles north of the bridge on Highway 101, you will cross three such drowned valleys. Large areas of the towns of Mill Valley, Corte Madera, and San Rafael have each been built on soil which was once part of Mount Tamalpais and was carried by streams to the edges of drowned valleys, where it became first marsh, then dry land.

Directly across the bay is another example of the way the streams are changing the shoreline. A five-mile-long ridge known as Potrero San Pablo rises five hundred feet above the bay and was probably at one time an island. Mainland streams built deltas out from the shore until they reached across the intervening strait and converted the island into a peninsula. Part of the city of Richmond now occupies much of this delta land. The largest of the bay's stream-built marshes are those at its extreme ends. Most of the peninsula cities along El Camino Real, three and four miles from the present shoreline, were constructed in areas which were at the water's edge before the bay was pushed back.

Considering only the advance of the marshes and the sedimentation of the bay, one might easily conclude that the river and its allies were winning their battle to reclaim the bay from the ocean and convert it into a valley again. But the ocean, meantime, is engaged in a counteraction of its own.

At several places around the shores are large artificial mounds which offer significant clues to the bay's future. They are the remains of Indian villages. There archaeologists have uncovered great quantities of clam and mussel shells, ashes from campfires, crude household implements, and human skeletons—all representing the residue of the centuries before the coming of the white man.

Such mounds are common in California, but some of the specimens found around the bay were distinguished by one curious fact: at least ten of them, on both sides of the bay, were partly submerged. One mound near Richmond—about six hundred feet long, thirty feet high and estimated to have contained three thousand human skeletons—was two thirds under water at high tide.

Archaeologists were puzzled. The Indians would scarcely have chosen to live on a site covered by water; they would have occupied an area of the beach at least high enough so that they would not be sprayed by waves at high tide.

There seemed to be only one explanation: The bay had risen some twenty-five or thirty feet since the mounds were first occupied about three thousand five hundred years ago. The rate of rise—slightly less than one tenth of an inch a year —tallied roughly with the calculated elevation of sea level from the melting of the ice sheet.

Thus it appears that the process which created the bay is still going on. The weather continues to get warmer; glacial ice all over the world melts (mountain glaciers on the Sierra peaks have been irregularly retreating inch by inch since they were first discovered and measured by John Muir in 1871) and the sea advances on the land.

These, then, are the primary forces arrayed on each side in the struggle for the bay's future. The river and the streams are tending to diminish the bay by depositing sediment on the bottom and building deltas at certain points around its edges; the ocean meantime is tending to make the bay larger by raising the water level and, in areas where there is no stream sedimentation, is actually advancing on the land.

The Deluge   The outcome of this war of the elements is uncertain, but distinct trends can be noted.

At present the river is the swifter of the two forces. Its sedimentation can be observed over a period of decades; the ocean's advance—slowing down because of the shrinkage of the icecap—can be measured only in thousands of years.

Consequently, if the two forces continue to work at their present rate, the river will be an easy victor. Relatively soon, possibly within a few thousand years, it will drive the ocean back out of the Gate; the valley floor will roughly correspond with the level of the present bay.

But the river's victory will be short-lived. For, if the ocean continued to rise until all the earth's ice were melted, it would eventually stand more than one hundred feet above its present level. It would again push through the Golden Gate, invade the valley, and rise to new heights, creating a bay more than twice as large as the present one.

If this eventuality comes to pass, the fate of the Indians' shell mounds will befall the cities of their successors. Year by year high tides will reach new levels. Beaches such as

San Francisco's Aquatic Park will disappear first. Homes built on low, filled areas around the margins of the bay—if they still stand—will have water first at their doorsteps, then at their window sills.

Man-made Treasure Island will be submerged relatively soon, and eventually only the highest peak of Alcatraz will be visible above the swirling waters at low tide. Waves will roll through the streets of peninsula cities, and although the University of California, at the foot of the Berkeley Hills, will stand above the high-tide mark, most of the Stanford campus, at Palo Alto, will be submerged, giving U.C. rooters their final triumph. The bay will extend southward beyond San Jose, filling most of the Santa Clara Valley, and northward will overflow into the Russian River, forty miles from the present shore.

In San Francisco the waters will surround the Ferry Building and creep up Market Street, spreading out in the low regions until the downtown area is a cluster of islands formed by the peaks of Nob, Telegraph, and Russian hills, and only the top stories of the tallest skyscrapers protrude from the bay's surface—remnants of a drowned city.

If the bay level continues to rise at the present rate, this deluge will be complete in a short time—possibly ten thousand years.

This picture of the death and rebirth of the bay is, of course, highly speculative. It presumes that the river will continue to deposit sediment and the sea will continue to rise, but it is possible that neither process will be carried through to completion. Man himself may slow down or eliminate sedimentation by dredging or diverting the rivers upstream. On the other hand, he may himself continue to fill in the bay for building purposes, replacing the river as the agent of the bay's destruction. Even so, he would still face the threat of the rising ocean.

It is possible, however, that before the ocean drowns the

coastal cities, it will cease to rise. As has happened several times in the past million years, the weather may cool off and the ice may return. Then the ocean would withdraw again and leave the bay dry until the next big thaw.

But by that time another force may re-enter the picture to alter the entire landscape in unpredictable ways—the changing crust of the earth itself.

Look out again from Land's End at the relic rocks of the Farallones and remember that in the long reaches of geologic time even mountain ranges are scarcely more permanent than waves on the surface of the ocean. The Coast Range may rise to new heights; it may be recast into unrecognizable new shapes; it may erode away and again become sea bottom. Then the cycle which began when the range first appeared above the surface of the ocean will be complete.

The larger forces of nature are as yet unalterable by man. The best he can now hope to do is to retard some of the minor processes and speed up others, puttering around the margins, allying himself now with one force, now with another, in his lifelong attempt to make his brief existence on earth more comfortable.

Until such time as he is able to affect the motions of the planet's crust and the changes in its sheath of atmosphere, the only certainty regarding San Francisco Bay is that, like every other feature of the landscape, it is transient. In time it will give way to newer forms just as surely as will the trees which bend before its winds or the human beings who now live on its shores.

THE PLANS OF MEN

Future aeons of geologic time, like the immeasurable distances of interstellar space, are scarcely comprehensible in terms of human purposes. Intriguing though they may be as speculation, they bear little relationship to the time scheme within which the mind of man must operate at the practical level.

Whatever is to be its fate in thousands or millions of years, the present bay has special significance of its own for the people who now live on its shores. Though men may be powerless to affect the long-term geologic future, they can alter the bay's shoreline in many ways; depending on the wisdom with which they plan, they can enhance or destroy, in varying degrees, its value as a place to live.

The Shrinking Bay   Ever since the first forty-niner hauled some dirt from the foot of Telegraph Hill and dumped it into Yerba Buena Cove, thereby making himself owner of a valuable waterfront lot, men have been remolding the bay's shores, extending them outward and carving them in various ways for harbors and ship channels.

Much of downtown San Francisco rests on bay bottom. The waterfront was gradually moved from the original beach along the line of Montgomery Street half a mile into the bay. North Beach, too, now high and dry, was once a real beach just northwest of Telegraph Hill. Much of the debris from the earthquake and fire of 1906 was dumped into the cove there, and workmen excavating for the Aquatic Park in the late 1930s dug up remains of the disaster, even including watches, jewelry, and foreign coins.

Most of San Francisco's Marina District was once part of the bay and was filled in for the Panama-Pacific International Exposition of 1915, from which is left only the crumbling but still-impressive Palace of Fine Arts. South of the Ferry Building the Mission Rock ship terminal is the only reminder of now-filled Mission Bay, the original anchorage for Mission Dolores.

An opposite process created the island of Alameda, a peninsula until 1902, when the Oakland estuary was extended around its southern end. Both San Francisco and Oakland airports were built where until recently tidal water flowed through winding channels, and farther south along the peninsula postwar subdivisions are increasingly occupying thousands of acres of drained marshes. The city of Berkeley plans to drain and develop several square miles of bay bottom, and most of the other communities along the shores have similar projects.

The current rapid encroachment of residential subdivisions and industrial sites raises a serious question about the bay's future. Although its size has not yet been appreciably diminished, planners must consider how much of the bay it is desirable to fill in. Conceivably it would be feasible to drain or fill all of it not necessary to shipping; and if present trends continue, this is a distinct possibility. But it is not necessarily a desirable one.

For most of the bay to be replaced by mile after mile of solidly built-up suburbs would be to eliminate the area's greatest natural advantage. The bay is not only useful as a harbor; it has other functions as well. It is in effect a huge untrodden park, offering space, perspective, and beauty— items which are not usually visible on a balance sheet and which will inevitably become increasingly rare as California's population increases to three or four times its present size. In the metropolitan regions such areas of natural space as still remain—and this includes the bay—should be jealously husbanded.

This does not mean that there should be an end to tideland development but rather that development should be planned to take advantage of the opportunities offered by the bay's presence. The possibilities of the shoreline for parks, beach resorts, and waterfront homesites have been scarcely explored.

Toward a Planned Shoreline   Unfortunately most of the developers of newly subdivided areas have simply dumped fill material into the water and built on top of it. Residents might as well live in the middle of Kansas for all the use that is made of the bay.

There have been encouraging exceptions, however. The first residential area to be developed with an imaginative eye for the potentialities of bay-front living was Belvedere Lagoon. The lagoon was partly filled by man-made peninsulas, and houses were built along the water, many with private docks in their back yards. A similar development on a much larger scale is Alameda's South Shore Project, a complete community built on filled land, including 1000 homes—some of which will be directly on lagoons—shopping centers, schools, and parks, plus a public beach on the perimeter. An even larger project is planned immediately south on the tidelands of Bay Farm Island.

Even these well-planned communities present problems, however. The South Shore Project caused a furor among residents of the original waterfront whose bay outlook was blocked. And the Bay Farm Island development is to occupy tidal flats which have long been one of the region's principal way stations for migratory waterfowl. Admittedly it is more important to provide homes for people than campsites for birds, but certainly consideration should be given in other areas to the preservation of some of the few remaining natural shores for the study and observation of the abundant wild life as well as for recreational areas for the great majority of bay area residents not able to live along the shores.

Richardson Bay, for example, is the prize in a desperate

race between developers, who want to fill it in, and residents of Marin who are carrying on a campaign to make its remaining edges a state park for small-boat landings, recreational beaches, and a wild-life refuge. The conservationists, as always, face an uphill struggle against those who see in the natural shores only a chance to plant more buildings. And they fight a frequently losing battle against time. The few shores available for parks are fast disappearing.

Fortunately the most spectacular and historic section of the bay's shores, the Golden Gate, has so far largely been spared from the subdividers. The entire north shore is in the hands of the Army, which has thus far left most of the area in its natural state. The Army's Presidio occupies much of the south side of the Gate, and most of the shoreline there is still in a relatively natural condition, although San Francisco interests have exerted increasing pressure in recent years to acquire the Presidio or parts of it for subdivision purposes, and the Army itself is expanding its own housing projects there.

Farther west San Francisco-owned Land's End has similarly been spared, except for some ill-fated attempts to build roads along the cliffs in slide areas. These ocean-battered cliffs and the rock-strewn beaches below them offer a magnificent exhibit of the continuing action of some of the processes which formed the bay, as the ocean rollers constantly attack the headlands, exposing twisted layers of rock laid down in the ages before the river carved this gorge. It would seem fitting that both shores of the Golden Gate—or at least as much of the area as is no longer necessary for defense purposes—be incorporated into a state or national park, while there is still time to preserve this incomparable shoreline against all encroachment.

Reber's Dream   All other plans for the bay, past and future, are mere puttering compared to the Paul Bunyan-sized schemes of John Reber. For half a century Reber has explored the bay's shores, sailed its currents, and devoted his major energies to studying it from every point of view. For more than half that time he has crusaded with all the energy of a barnstorming evangelist on behalf of his prodigious project to remodel the bay—the Reber Plan.

In the perennial conflict between the river and the ocean —the geologic war in which the bay is the pawn and prize— Reber is a strong partisan. His purpose is to push the ocean out of most of the bay basin and reclaim it for the river. He would do so by building two earth-and-rock dams across the narrow necks of the upper and lower bay, one from San Francisco to Oakland, one from the Richmond area to Marin. The dams would be broad enough to carry all the traffic that would ever cross the bay, including main-line railroads and rapid-transit lines.

Fresh water flowing down from the river through Carquinez would soon flush out the salt water above the northern dam and make that part of the bay a fresh-water reservoir. From there a ship canal would carry river water down the east shore to the area below the San Francisco-Oakland dam, making a second fresh-water lake. Thus, says Reber, California's urgent water problem would be disposed of forever by conserving at least one third of the tremendous volume of fresh water which now rushes down from the Sierra to the bay and wastes out the Golden Gate. The bay area would have at its doorstep reservoirs with a total surface area greater than any man-made lake on earth, constantly replenished by the river, "with all the water the state can ever use," says Reber, "free for the pumping."

Besides transportation and water the Reber Plan would provide, according to its author, a fantastic array of other benefits: thousands of acres of new filled land for airports, factories, and military bases; a single "grand central" terminal for rail, ship, air, and bus lines; many miles of warm-water bathing beaches, and lakeside sites for resort hotels and homes. From Reber's fresh-water lakes a canal would run down the west side of the San Joaquin Valley to supply water for the rest of the state, tunneling through the Tehachapis to Los Angeles and to San Diego, five hundred miles away. Paralleling the canal would run a direct-line super-freeway over which it would be possible to drive to Los Angeles in five hours, about half the time required at present.

Reber's ambition goes even further. "The water in these lakes, you know, would warm to the average of the temperature in the surrounding area. Hot days . . . would be cooler and the cool days would be warmer. I can change the climate," he says with a grin, adding, with classic understatement: "This is quite a project."

There are those who dismiss the whole project with a terse judgment: "Reber is crazy." There are many others who think he is about as crazy as Columbus. A U. S. Senate subcommittee looking into the plan in 1949 found it of sufficient merit to convince Congress to vote funds for a long-term study of the bay, including the Reber Plan. As dramatized by its dynamic author, the plan has fired the imaginations of tens of thousands of Californians throughout the state.

The Crusade   John Reber was eighteen years old when he first saw the bay; he sailed into the Golden Gate in 1907, and his energetic mind soon was intrigued by the possibilities of improving on what nature had wrought. As the youngster paced the hills of the city overlooking the bay, it struck him as absurd that the main-line railroads did not come into San Francisco but were halted in Oakland several miles short of their logical terminus. The solution seemed simple: San Francisco and Oakland should be united by land; an earthen dam across the bay would fill the gap that nature left. Thus the first unit of the Reber Plan was born.

For twenty-five years, as Reber traveled throughout the state, making his living by producing amateur theatricals, the plan slowly evolved in his mind. In spare moments he supplemented his high-school education by devouring books on engineering, water resources, and transportation.

Finally, encouraged by an interview with Herbert Hoover, he abandoned theatricals and hit the sawdust trail for the Reber Plan. Maps underneath his arm, he hiked from office to office, enlisting businessmen, publishers, political officials, military leaders. The plan was his Bible and he was its prophet. In an emotion-charged voice he presented his idea to hundreds of clubs, schools, churches, and civic groups. Chambers of commerce, women's clubs, granges, and farm bureaus passed resolutions in favor of the plan, and it became the subject of countless laudatory editorials and articles.

Like most crusaders, Reber had enemies. His most vociferous opponents were representatives of Oakland, Alameda, Richmond, and Stockton, whose ports would be left behind Reber's dams. Their shipping traffic would have to pass through locks, resulting, they believed, in expensive delays. Similarly taking a dim view of the plan were officials of industries which would be handicapped or destroyed by it, including the south-bay salt plant and chemical plants using bay water. Fishermen complained that the plan would wipe out the major game and commercial fish in the bay—striped bass, salmon, steelhead, herring, and shrimp.

Conceivably all these objections could be discounted if the Reber Plan were to break, once and for all, the traffic bottleneck caused by the bay and at the same time were to furnish an ample supply of the water that California must have for its future growth. But Reber's opponents believe that his proposed forty lanes of highway traffic across the two dams would be needless and extravagant; they claim that present and planned bridges can adequately handle all future traffic. And many railroad officials feel that the expense and readjustments involved in bringing the rails across the bay would not be justified by any corresponding benefits. With characteristic fervor Reber scoffs at the skeptics as shortsighted and unable to visualize the unlimited future growth of the region.

As to water, the state engineers are convinced that Reber's lakes would not furnish a consistent usable supply. If the river's flow into the bay were constant and steady, there would be no problem. But its wild inconsistency from season to season and from year to year causes the engineers to shake their heads at Reber's scheme. They maintain that in the dry season of the driest year in a cycle of dry years, when the river flow was extremely low, it would not be sufficient to keep the lakes fresh; even if ways were found to dispose of all the domestic and industrial wastes now dumped into the bay, the water at such times would be too salty for either drinking or irrigation purposes.

These objections reveal the basic difference in approach between the state engineers and Reber. The engineers assume that it is necessary to guarantee to consumers a continuous flow through all the months of every year; their studies were therefore based on the water supply that would have been available during the seven-year drought period 1928–34. Reber, however, counts the water he believes he can salvage over and above the amount that would be available in such a drought. During the times of ample flow he would catch vast amounts of water to be pumped out of his lakes and stored for use during the cyclic dry periods, either in surface reservoirs or in the natural underground basins, building up the water table in areas where it is now sinking fast. He further points out that the extreme dry period on which the engineers base their calculations has occurred only once in a hundred years.

Neither Reber himself nor the state engineers have investigated the problems involved in capturing the river's flow in the way the Reber Plan proposes. In order to hold back any large proportion of the winter floods it would be necessary to build pumping plants probably far larger than any ever constructed. River-sized canals would have to be built to distribute the water. And no one knows how many storage reservoirs would be necessary or to what extent natural underground basins could absorb the flow.

The unprecedented size of these distribution facilities, which would be used to capacity only for brief periods during the heavy flow of winter, is considered by the state engineers to make them so expensive as to be not worth investigation. They believe that sufficient water for the state's growth can be supplied more cheaply by building more mountain reservoirs, as contemplated in the official California Water Plan.

Which plan would supply the greatest benefits for the money spent remains an unanswered question, and the value of both plans would have to be reappraised if scientists should develop economic ways to convert salt water into fresh.

The Bay Model   Further evidence as to whether the Reber Plan is feasible will come out of a big warehouse in Sausalito, where the Army Corps of Engineers, as part of the congressionally authorized survey of the bay, has constructed a minutely accurate, acre-sized, concrete scale model of the bay and its shores, patterned after the corps's highly successful models of Eastern river and bay areas.

By taking careful measurements and making mathematical adjustments to apply the model findings to the bay itself it will be possible to evaluate the effects of Reber-type barriers on salinity, tides, currents, and shoaling. Problems not dealt with on the model will be investigated in supplementary engineering studies. The entire job is scheduled to be finished by 1960.

On the model most of the channels are only a few inches in depth, but so deep is the bay's entrance that workmen "building" the Golden Gate had to cut a hole in the floor of the warehouse to accommodate it. Salt water can be pumped in through the Gate and fresh water from the river through Carquinez in the exact proportions of nature. Here man can play God, creating tides and floods at the twist of a valve, duplicating the bay's entire tidal cycle in fifteen minutes.

No one is more fascinated by the operations of this indoor bay than old John Reber. He often paces the warehouse floor, gazing over the model, just as he paced the hills overlooking the bay a half century ago, formulating the elements of his plan. Here, before his eyes, the Reber Plan will be constructed in miniature. And here, he is convinced, his long crusade to remake the bay will be finally vindicated.

ACCENTS

The sounds of the bay are the high-pitched whistles of tugs and the bass bellows of ocean liners and foghorns . . . the creaking of winches and the yells of the longshoremen along the Embarcadero . . . the thunder of giant combers on the rocks at Land's End . . . the quiet lapping of wavelets on the docks at Sausalito . . . the metallic roar of commuter trains on the lower deck of the Bay Bridge . . . the noonday siren of the Ferry Building . . . the cries of gulls as they wheel around crab boats coming loaded into Fisherman's Wharf . . . the throaty roar of the sea lions at Seal Rocks . . . the aeolian music of a high wind in the harp-string cables of the Golden Gate Bridge . . .

The smells of the bay are the aroma of roasting coffee early in the morning at the San Francisco end of the Bay Bridge . . . the fresh salt fragrance of the west wind through

*the Gate on a summer afternoon . . . the smell of a grilled
fish dinner and boiled crabs along Fisherman's Wharf . . .
the heavy, sweet smell of chocolate from the Ghirardelli plant
at Aquatic Park . . . the acrid odor of the north-bay oil refineries, sometimes borne across to the city on a northerly
breeze . . . the pungent, soapy smell of copra from the docks
at the mouth of Islais Creek . . . the odor of tules and other
marsh plants in the sloughs of the delta . . . the tang of
spray as it breaks over the bow of a sailboat leaning before the
wind off Angel Island . . . the smell of damp mosses and sea-
weed at low tide on any of the bay's hundreds of miles of
shoreline . . . the cool night fragrance of the fog as it rolls
through the Gate, spills into the Marina, and swirls slowly up
the steep streets of Pacific Heights, enveloping the old mansions in a veil of privacy.*

11

Islands of Time

From Ulysses to Robinson Crusoe to *South Pacific,* islands—real or mythical—have appealed to the human imagination with the fascination of the unknown.

California itself existed as an island in legend long before it was actually discovered; the men of Cortez who saw the tip of the long peninsula off the west coast of Mexico believed it to be the fabled isle California, "on the right hand side of the Indies," peopled with Amazons and paved with gold.

In a lesser way the islands of San Francisco Bay have long stimulated speculation and myth. Many of them are surrounded by auras of legend, particularly tales of buried treasure and undiscovered deposits of gold.

Geologically, of course, the islands of the bay are merely high ridges or peaks that were isolated when the ocean moved in through the Golden Gate and rose in the river valley. But their isolation is more than geological. For more than a century they have been cut off in varying degrees from the tides of time and change that have swirled around the bay's shores, and the real treasure, the genuine fascination to be found in these islands, is the peculiar quality of time with which each of them in its own way seems to be haunted.

Some of them, almost completely by-passed by events of the past century, are curious remnants of an earlier age. Others combine the past and the future in striking juxtaposition. On one there lingers the spirit of the event which brought it into being and which itself was a bold projection into the future. On another, time and events speed along with frenetic acceleration. And on yet another, time is strangely out of kilter; its inhabitants are acutely conscious of clocks and calendars, yet live in a wholly different time scheme from that of the shoreline cities they can see beyond the cold racing waters of the bay.

THE ROCK

One Friday morning early in May of 1946 hundreds of San Franciscans stood on Telegraph Hill and other vantage points overlooking the bay, peering intently at the federal penitentiary on Alcatraz, a mile offshore. Occasionally their vigilance was rewarded by the sound of gunfire, muffled explosions, puffs of smoke, and the visible figures of running men. Word had spread quickly through the city that the convicts had captured many of the guards and were trying to take over the island.

The fascination of the spectators was mixed with apprehension; if the convicts succeeded, would they then head for the city?

Most of the onlookers had never had any more idea of what went on behind the walls of Alcatraz than they had of what transpired inside the Kremlin. Their only sources of information were occasional lurid magazine articles in which the place was described—usually by a writer who had never been any closer to it than had his readers—as "America's torture chamber" and likened to such other infamous island prisons as Byron's Castle of Chillon and Dumas's Château d'If. It was understandable, then, that bay area residents watched the island that morning in May with nervous curiosity.

The Battle of Alcatraz   Inside the big cell house on the island's peak the previous afternoon three convicts had overpowered three guards, one by one, and seized a Springfield rifle and a .45 automatic. Then they began to unlock the doors of the cells.

"The cons have taken over the joint!" one of the inmates yelled. "Let's go!"

The ringleaders planned to unlock the prison yard, release the mass of convicts, pick off the tower guards and take complete control of the island. But they were unable to find the crucial key to the yard. One of the captured guards had hidden it and despite continued beatings refused to tell where it was.

The leaders were desperate. "I can't find the damned key," one of them yelled, "so we're all fouled up and Frisco's as far away as ever!"

Had the key been found, the battle might have ended differently. But the game was far from over. One by one the convicts waylaid and tied up six more guards who had sensed trouble and come to investigate. So skillfully did the prisoners maneuver that prison headquarters did not discover what had happened until nearly an hour after the original break. Warden James Johnston then quickly sounded the alarm, mobilized his remaining guard force, and organized an attack on the cell block where the mutinous prisoners were barricaded. In the gun battle that followed three guards were wounded and one killed, but the escaped convicts warily kept hidden.

All day the opposing forces maneuvered for position, occasionally firing a few shots. Late that night the guards finally blasted their way to where their captured colleagues were tied up. One of the convicts in a burst of fury had shot six of them with his revolver; four of the six were critically wounded.

Faced with such opposition, Warden Johnston called for help, and a contingent of U. S. Marines arrived from Treasure Island. They climbed to the roof of the cell block, drilled holes and dropped grenades. From the lawn outside other marines fired rifle grenades into the building; some of the ammunition hit the wall, bounced off, and set the dry grass aflame. Billows of smoke arose, and spectators in San Francisco thought the prison was on fire.

Most of the prisoners who had been released had long since returned to their cells, realizing that escape was hopeless, but the original three took refuge in a utility corridor among a maze of pipes, ventilators, and conduits, ignoring demands to surrender.

By daylight Saturday morning Warden Johnston decided the time had come to make the final rush. Two officers opened the corridor door and peered into the darkness. Shouts brought no response. They sprayed the corridor with gunfire, then ran inside. The place was a shambles of twisted, broken pipes, escaping water and steam. Sprawled in the darkness were the bodies of the three holdouts, still clutching the weapons that had enabled them to stand off the prison force for nearly two days. The Battle of Alcatraz had come to a grisly end. Two other inmates involved in the break were later tried and executed.

Residents of the bay area could again breathe easily. But the tragic episode set off some serious discussion. The big blowup of 1946 was the first visible evidence local residents had ever had of the explosive atmosphere of hatred, viciousness, and desperation that had existed for generations on the rocky island separated from San Francisco by only a mile of water. The result was a public reappraisal. What was behind the Battle of Alcatraz? And why had the prison been built there in the first place, so close to the city?

"Devil's Island"   Even before the prison was established, Alcatraz had always been a scowling, inhospitable place. Unlike most other bay islands, which were naturally well wooded, its gravelly soil supported only a few scrubby weeds. The Indians apparently avoided the island completely, and its barren cliffs were so unattractive to Ayala and his original survey party, based just a short distance away on Angel Island, that they not only avoided landing there but failed even to dignify the place with a name.

It later acquired its name by mistake. Ayala had given the title "Isla de Alcatraces" to the island now known as Yerba Buena, naming it for the great flocks of pelicans he saw there. When the next survey of the bay was completed by British Captain Frederick W. Beechey in 1826, the name was erroneously transferred to the rocky isle just inside the Golden Gate.

The Spanish and Mexicans, like the Indians, largely ignored the island, but enterprising Yankees built a lighthouse there, and the Army Engineers subsequently converted it into a small Gibraltar commanding the entrance to the bay.

The island's first prisoners, aside from casual soldier inmates of the post's guardhouse, were privateers. The schooner *J. M. Chapman* had been fitted out during the Civil War by Southern sympathizers in San Francisco in order to attack

Union commerce as part of a wild scheme to take Fort Alcatraz and Fort Scott and capture the bay for the Confederacy. But no sooner did the schooner cast off from the dock and swing into the stream than she was ingloriously taken into custody by Union vessels without firing a shot, and her crew of seventeen was promptly clapped into Alcatraz. Thus did the Union Navy win the Battle of San Francisco Bay with no more casualties than Frémont had incurred in "capturing" the city a few years earlier.

Not long afterward the Rock housed a batch of political prisoners. Democratic state convention orators, including the party's state chairman, were locked up for attacking the Republican administration's conduct of the war.

With the development of long-range artillery, making the island obsolete for harbor defense, Alcatraz evolved gradually from a fort to a disciplinary barracks to a military prison. Incarcerated behind its high walls at various times were unsubdued Indians from Arizona; Philippine war deserters; prisoners from San Francisco jails who were removed from the city during the disaster of 1906; and, during World War I, conscientious objectors, enemy aliens, spies, and San Francisco's German Consul General. Strangely, for a brief time in 1900, the island was also used as a health resort for convalescent soldiers.

Even before World War I, Alcatraz had been labeled "Uncle Sam's Devil's Island" in popular magazines, but it did not achieve its greatest fame as America's most feared prison until the 1930s, when some well-known names began to appear on its roster.

Federal authorities, looking for a "supermaximum security prison" where they could quarantine the worst of the Prohibition-era gangsters, found what they considered an ideal site in Alcatraz, which the War Department was then planning to abandon. There were vociferous objections from San Francisco and other bay area communities, and three female amphibians swam to the island at different times to prove that the bay's currents were not an effective barrier to escape. Actually, of course, they proved no such thing; all three were athletes in top physical shape, had long trained for the feat, and swam across the channel during the slack tide and in good weather in full view of anyone who happened to be looking—conditions which prisoners could hardly hope to duplicate successfully.

In 1934 sealed trains arrived at the bay's north shore and were barged across to the island, disgorging "incorrigible" prisoners from Atlanta, Leavenworth, and other federal penitentiaries. Among them was Al Capone, who became the Rock's best-known resident. The Chicago mobster soon found that his talent for organization (in the Atlanta penitentiary he had even organized prisoners into a personal bodyguard) was of little avail on the island, and he quickly sank into the anonymity of prison life. Like his fellow inmates, he scrubbed floors, carried library books, worked in the laundry, and swept the recreation yard. He spent the final years of his ten-year felony sentence in the prison hospital under treatment for an old illness and died in Florida not long after his release.

Among other guests on the island were such notables in America's hall of infamy as Machine-Gun Kelly, Roy Gardner, "Creepy" Karpis, and Basil "The Owl" Banghart, who had bragged that no prison could hold him but who found out different.

Ingenious Escapes   Among the escapes from Alcatraz while it was still in the hands of the Army was one of the most improbable breaks ever engineered. Four prisoners who worked in the administrative offices carefully made out documents recommending their own release, forged the commandant's signature, and slipped the applications into the outgoing mail. High Army officials in Washington were so impressed with the good recommendations that they sent orders back to Alcatraz for the release of the four. The commandant was puzzled, but as an old soldier he followed orders.

The four men, probably astonished that their daring ruse had actually succeeded, were put on the boat to San Francisco and walked jubilantly free into the city. They headed for a saloon to celebrate their triumph, and one of them became so drunk that he began bragging loudly about the achievement. The others were unable to shut him up and fled. The drunk was picked up and returned to the Rock, but the other three were never heard of again.

After Alcatraz became a federal prison, escape attempts were considerably less successful. One of the would-be escapees who got the farthest was a shrewd fifty-year-old lone operator named John K. Giles, who dreamed up an elaborate Charlie Chaplin-type routine for his break. He had a job sweeping the dock area, which enabled him to piece together over a long period of time a complete Army uniform from the military laundry brought in by boat from nearby posts.

One morning when the regular boat arrived Giles jumped under the wharf, quickly pulled off his overalls, revealing the uniform, and slipped onto the boat. There, mingling with some Army technicians who had been working on the island's phone cable, he took a notebook and pencil from his pocket and assiduously made notes until the boat pulled away.

During the trip he found a seat, gazed nonchalantly out at the bay, and chatted with other soldiers aboard. Impressed by his age, confident bearing, and the staff sergeant's chevrons on his sleeve, they accepted his story that he was a special cable lineman from another unit.

Meanwhile, back on the dock, a guard discovered that Giles

was missing. Puzzled, he searched around and under the pier but found nothing. He gazed suspiciously after the departing boat, now halfway to Angel Island. Then the truth dawned, and he hustled to a phone to give the alarm. The associate warden jumped into a speedboat and arrived on the Angel Island dock just in time to see the passengers file off the Alcatraz boat and line up in formation. He walked down the line of soldiers, peering into their faces, and spotted Giles, standing smartly at attention and looking straight ahead. The other soldiers stared in amazement as the handcuffs were clamped on and the impressive-looking staff sergeant became an Alcatraz convict once again.

Most escape attempts were much more grim affairs. An extraordinary combination of desperation and patience was demonstrated in 1939 by kidnaper "Doc" Barker and four cohorts. They were caught on the island's rocky shores after having slowly cut their way through the steel bars of their cells with abrasive dust rubbed back and forth under string. Two of them were wounded by guards. Barker left the island, but not as he had planned. He departed in a pine box, riddled by bullets.

Four years later a quartet of bank bandits got a little farther. A guard spotted two of them swimming energetically about two hundred yards offshore, towing watertight cans containing clothing. One of them sank with a bullet in his head; the other was picked up by the prison launch; and a third was flushed out of a cave near the water's edge. The fourth was assumed to have drowned until two days later when he meekly crawled back in a window, numb, hungry, and badly cut by barbed wire, rocks, and debris in the shoreline cave where he had spent an agonizing forty-eight hours.

Into the Fog   The most mysterious—and the only conceivably successful—escape case since Alcatraz became a federal penitentiary has never been solved. Ralph Roe and Theodore Cole had been incarcerated together in two previous penitentiaries, and as escape artists functioned as a smoothly working team. Roe, a big bank bandit, supplied the brawn, and diminutive Cole, a kidnaper twelve years younger, gave the orders.

Compared with some of the elaborate escape attempts which failed, their plan was marvelously simple. One afternoon in December of 1937 they simply smashed a window overlooking the bay, dropped down to a path outside, broke a gate with a wrench, slid down the cliff to the beach below, and disappeared before the alarm was sounded.

Whether by accident or design the two had picked one of the foggiest days in the bay's history to make their break. A dense tule fog had brought shipping traffic to a standstill. The prison launch, police, and Coast Guard boats nosed slowly through the thick vapors, circling the island. They found nothing; crews could scarcely see the bows of their boats. An inch-by-inch search of the island was fruitless.

Police and sheriff's deputies patrolled shores around the bay, pointing headlights and floodlights into the fog, seeing nothing. A boat loaded with curious newspaper reporters blundered too near the island and was fired on by nervous guards. In the next few days hundreds of reports came in from all over the state that men answering the description of Cole and Roe had been seen, but none of the reports checked out. No valid clues ever turned up, and although no bodies were ever found, the two were presumed to have drowned. But there was an odd twist to the story.

Four years after the escape, a San Francisco newspaperman reported that he had learned, presumably from a former Alcatraz inmate, that the two convicts after slipping through the fence had picked up on the beach two airtight oil cans with civilian clothes, used the cans as floats, and made their

way, possibly on a small boat waiting offshore, to Marin
County. There confederates supplied them with a car; they
picked up loot they had hidden before their arrest and made
their way by a circuitous route to Mexico. Four other Alcatraz
convicts had seen a letter from Roe and Cole which gave
the word in a prearranged code that they had made good
their escape. At that time, the reporter wrote, the two were
living comfortably in South America.

Could the story have been true? Consider the odds: The
two convicts would have had to swim three miles to the nearest point on the Marin mainland, in racing currents, through
the icy water of December, towing two oil cans. Or they
would have had to communicate through the walls of the
prison to confederates on shore and arrange for a boat to
find them in the water in the dense fog at the exact moment
they were able to make the break. And they would have had
to make their way through thickly populated areas past road
blocks and the dragnet set up by the FBI and state and local
police.

The odds that they failed are overwhelming. There seems
little doubt that they drowned. Yet it is conceivably possible
that in some remote foreign city there are two Americans,
one tall, one short, whose pasts are unknown. . . .

Life behind the Wall   Every few years the warden holds
"open house" for the press, and newsmen are given a guided
tour of the island. From what reporters see life on Alcatraz
bears scant resemblance to the Devil's Island legend.

The nation's "toughest convicts" work an eight-hour day
in the prison's industrial shops. They can congregate and chat
during the two daily rest breaks, and on Saturday afternoons
and Sundays they can roam the high-walled prison yard.
Movies are scheduled twice a month and selected radio
broadcasts are piped into earphones in the cells during the

leisure hours from 6 to 9:30 in the evenings. During this period the inmates are allowed to read books or magazines, properly censored. They may also write or paint—a hobby which a few have pursued so diligently that their work has been exhibited in San Francisco art shows.

The cell blocks are light and clean, and their color (in the choice of which the convicts were not consulted) is shocking pink. Prison officers and their families are housed in pastel-painted modern apartments on the island's south side; children scamper and shout at their games (although they are forbidden to have any knives or cap pistols) and commute on the prison launch to school in San Francisco.

Yet Alcatraz is still the Rock, and the threat of a sentence there is still used to enforce discipline in other federal prisons. An infraction of the rules can land an inmate in dreaded solitary confinement. The old "dungeons" hewn from the island's rock in the basement of the cell block are no longer used, but a stretch in solitary is still formidable; a man is sent to "the hole" to think over his infraction in complete darkness on a meager diet of watery stew.

Communication with the outside world is limited to censored letters and once-a-month visits from immediate relatives, who can talk only through an aperture in a glass wall while guards listen. One other avenue is open; if a prisoner thinks his legal rights have been violated, he can petition the courts. Many petitions are simply normal complaints about food or other prison conditions, and the courts refuse to intervene. But some have been successful in springing a prisoner off the Rock.

The most persistent petitioner in the prison's history was Cecil Wright, convicted of a drugstore robbery in Illinois in 1929 and given a federal sentence because the loot included $2.45 worth of postage stamps. In his Alcatraz cell Wright secured some lawbooks, studied up on habeas corpus, and wrote petitions so assiduously that the court eventually ordered him released.

Later, however, he was hauled back on a technicality. He got out the lawbooks again and bombarded the court with petitions, earning the title of "Writ-a-Day" Wright. Finally in 1948 he was again successful and was set free after having served nearly half his life in prison, most of it under the sentence that the court pronounced invalid.

The U. S. Attorney whom Wright had finally bested after innumerable encounters shook his head and confessed that Wright was "the world's greatest authority on habeas corpus."

Other famous latter-day residents of the Rock are Morton Sobell, convicted as an atom spy in a controversial case, and Robert Stroud, like Wright a top authority on a specialized subject. Convicted of murder in 1909, Stroud killed a prison guard at Leavenworth in a fight in 1916, was saved from execution by President Wilson, and has spent the last forty years in segregated confinement. He took up bird study as a prison hobby, became a nationally known expert on bird diseases and wrote two books on the subject. His own life became the subject of a book, *Birdman of Alcatraz,* by Thomas E. Gaddis, scheduled for motion-picture production.

Alcatraz Is Obsolete   Bay area residents are far from unanimous on the question of Alcatraz. Some continue to believe that the prison should be abandoned as a danger to bay area communities. Others say it should stay—as a landmark and a tourist attraction. Many, probably the majority, are indifferent. And probably all three groups are wrong.

It does not seem likely—in view of the record—that escaped prisoners will constitute a great danger to bay communities. There are far better reasons for believing that the prison should be abandoned—the sooner the better.

The main cell house, on top of the island, inherited from

the Army, is almost half a century old and was built on the foundations of earlier structures dating back to the Civil War. The cornerstone of one of the old buildings reads: "Alcatraces 1857." The passing of each year brings new cracks in the walls and the necessity for more repairs. The expense of maintaining a prisoner on the island is more than twice that of other federal penitentiaries.

And the prison is obsolete in an even more important respect. The reason it became a penitentiary—to house the mobsters of the 1930s—no longer exists. Built to hold five hundred, it is often less than half full. Many of its present inhabitants could by no conceivable logic be classed with the Prohibition-era gangsters for whom the prison was established.

Take, for example, the record of a prisoner named Floyd P. Wilson, who created headlines in 1956 when he disappeared and was believed to have escaped to the mainland. In 1947 Wilson was an unemployed carpenter living with his wife and five young children in an unheated house in fifteen-degree weather. He had no previous criminal record, but, to get money to buy some coal, he tried to hold up a grocery employee, bungled the job, shot the grocer—accidentally, he claimed—and fled home without taking the money. Convicted of murder, he was serving a life term at the time of his 1956 attempted escape. That job, too, he bungled. After twelve hours guards found him in one of the island's water-level caves, shivering and hungry. Unable to swim, he was as terrified of the water as he was of the prison.

The sole function of Alcatraz is punishment; it is without facilities for education or rehabilitation; it was designed to house "incorrigibles," a concept which many criminologists believe to be itself obsolete. The very fact that many of the inmates are eventually released to freedom would seem to be tacit acknowledgment by prison authorities that they are not incurable criminals. Yet because of inadequate facilities no effort can be made during their Alcatraz terms to train them to take their places in society.

Although prison administrators at Alcatraz have been on the whole enlightened, the very fact that they have so nearly absolute power over the inmates makes some abuses almost inevitable. The secrecy which surrounds the island is seldom penetrated. When in the early years of the prison a group of men refrained from eating, as a gesture of protest, food was forced down them through tubes.

Alcatraz is a symbol of an outmoded era in penology. For nearly two decades there has been talk of abandoning the prison. As early as 1939 Attorney General Frank Murphy condemned Alcatraz as "a place of horror." Seventeen years later the Bureau of Prisons was still declaring its repeated intentions to vacate the Rock and move the inmates to a modern maximum-security prison, to be built somewhere in the Midwest. But the difficulty of getting money from Congress for prisons, residents of which can't vote, is notorious.

Meanwhile behind the high walls and barbed-wire fences of the Rock men cut off almost completely from the world of freedom which they can see so tantalizingly near, beyond the bay, continue to count the hours and years of confinement ahead. Others have lost all track of time and plod daily through the dull routine without hope. One prisoner wrote:

> Maybe you have asked yourself how can a man of even ordinary intelligence put up with this kind of life day in, day out, week after week, month after month, year after year. You might wonder whence do I draw sufficient courage to endure it.
>
> To begin with, these words seem written in fire on the walls of my cell: "Nothing can be worth this." No one knows what it is like to suffer from the intellectual atrophy, the pernicious mental scurvy that comes of long

privation of all the things that make life real, because even the analogy of thirst cannot possibly give you an inkling of what it is like to be tortured by the absence of everything that makes life worth living. A prisoner cannot keep from being haunted by a vision of life as it used to be when it was real and lovely. At such times I pay with a sense of overwhelming melancholy my tribute to life as it once was.

It has been suggested that, if the prison is ever moved, the island, commanding the entrance to the bay, would be an excellent site for a monument, perhaps, ironically, a Pacific-coast equivalent to the Statue of Liberty.

THE GEM OF THE BAY

Within the 640 hilly acres of Angel Island—exactly one square mile—are astonishing ranges of climate, geography, vegetation . . . and time.

You can stand on the southwest corner of the island assaulted by wind, fog, and icy salt spray, then within fifteen minutes walk to a cove on the northern shore where a genial sun warms a grassy glade beneath subtropical trees surrounded by exotic plants and flowers.

You can wander along trails overgrown by junglelike foliage and suddenly come upon large abandoned buildings, hidden in the matted tangle of trees and brush like the dwellings of some vanished race.

And you can walk a few hundred yards farther to a barren landscape where uniformed men work with weird devices—odd-shaped radar equipment and long guided missiles named for Nike, the goddess of victory. Quail run in the brush, and big black-tailed deer prowl trails through wooded glens, drink at hidden springs, and stare from the protection of thickets at the strange doings of men and machines.

"Los Angeles Island"   The activities observed by the deer are presumably a striking contrast to the doings of whatever angelic inhabitants the island may have had at an earlier date. Whether any winged hosts had actually been seen on their namesake isle was in the early days a subject open to speculation. Dr. Edwin Bentley, an Army surgeon stationed on the island, wrote in 1869:

> The name of the island has been supposed to have origi-
> nated from the sublimity of its scenery and the serenity
> of its climate, its perpetual foliage, and ever-blooming
> flowers. Also for its being the real habitation of Ghosts
> whose apparitions have been seen by the superstitious in
> the night season traveling about its sequestered walks or
> wandering around its wild and obscure retreats, occasion-
> ally appearing in open view of moonlight on the moun-
> tain slopes . . .

A later historian wrote solemnly that the name arose from the fact that the island "was considered a most angelic spot, where the inspiration of goodness seemed everywhere."

To Juan Manuel de Ayala, after he had sailed his little *San Carlos* through the unknown, rock-strewn waters of the Golden Gate for the first time in 1775, the island haven may have indeed seemed angelic, but he chose its name for other reasons. Following the custom of the Spanish explorers in naming geographical features for the saints, he called it: "Nuestra Señora de los Angeles." Thus the island had priority on the title that six years later was given to a village four hundred miles to the south. Early Americans called it "Los

Angeles Island." But eventually Yankee impatience shortened the name to Angel.

Whether by luck or intuition Ayala had selected as headquarters for his survey the island which later was aptly called "the gem of the bay." And the sheltered cove on the island's north side where he finally anchored had possibly the best climate in the bay area.

The next notable visitor to the island, Richard Henry Dana, was not enthusiastic about its climate, however. In *Two Years Before the Mast* he wrote of a miserable day and two nights he spent there, alternately frozen and drenched with rain, while gathering wood for his ship. Fourteen years after his visit the Gold Rush began, and so many gold hunters followed his example in wood gathering on the island that when he returned in 1859 he noted that it was "clean shorn of trees."

The Duel   Quick-tempered Californians of that era found other uses for the island as well. Its isolation and seclusion made it an excellent dueling ground. The most famous encounter there took place in 1858 and grew out of the white-hot issue of slavery.

A slave boy known only as Archy, who had been brought to California from Mississippi, escaped from a Sacramento River boat and became the center of a bitter controversy when authorities refused to return him to his master. The boy's owner went to court, and the Archy case ultimately reached U. S. Commissioner George Penn Johnson, who gave the boy his freedom.

The decision was furiously debated in every saloon in San Francisco. The most heated argument took place in a downtown tavern between Johnson himself and his good friend State Senator William I. Ferguson. The two were frequent drinking companions, and many a soiree had been climaxed by Johnson's dramatic recital of Scott's *Lady of the Lake* and Ferguson's rendition of a rollicking ballad called "Ipse-Doodle." But on this occasion poetry and song gave way to argument so fierce that Ferguson referred to Johnson in un-printable language, and the latter immediately challenged him to a duel. Ferguson, a Southern gentleman, upheld his honor by accepting.

The contest was made particularly ironic by the fact that Johnson was the author of an anti-dueling law which had been passed by the state legislature just four years previously.

Late on the afternoon of August 21 the principals met with dueling pistols on the eastern side of Angel Island inside Point Blunt. Probably both men had qualms about going through with the encounter but saw no honorable way out. They stood back-to-back in a small level clearing. From nearby came the sound of waves washing up on the beach where Dana had gathered wood on a frigid December morn-ing twenty-three years earlier. The late afternoon sun, oc-casionally veiled by wisps of fog floating overhead, threw long shadows on the clearing.

At the command the antagonists stepped off ten paces, turned and fired. The two shots echoed in the clearing and out across the bay. Both missed. Under the agreement the distance was then reduced to ten feet.

What thoughts ran through the minds of both men will never be known, but it is highly probable that neither found himself able to aim at his good friend and pull the trigger with the deliberate intention of hitting him. For whatever reason, each fired two more rounds at nearly point-blank range without hitting the other.

Johnson then offered to call the whole thing off if his op-ponent would apologize. But Ferguson could not humble himself by an apology and chose instead a fourth round. On this exchange both men were hit, Johnson in the left wrist and Ferguson in the right thigh.

Both then declared themselves satisfied, shook hands, and returned to San Francisco. Johnson's wound healed rapidly, but Ferguson's leg became steadily worse for three weeks until it was decided to amputate. He died as a result of the operation.

The conscience-stricken Johnson, tried under his own law, was acquitted on the ground that Ferguson had died not from the shot but from his own delay in agreeing to an amputation. As a result of the tragic encounter on Angel Island and the Terry-Broderick duel in San Francisco the following year, the dueling era in California came to an end.

Militant Angel As if further to belie its name the island's principal use in the past century has been for warlike purposes. It was the staging area for American soldiers in the Spanish-American War and both World Wars, and the island is still marked with deserted artillery emplacements, camps, and fortifications. Generations of soldiers were acutely aware of the island's climatic extremes; the camp on windy Point Blunt on the southeast corner was labeled Camp Consumption and later Camp Pneumonia. Sheltered Fort McDowell, only a few hundred yards north, on the old dueling ground, was commonly known as Camp Summer.

Near a beach on the western shore is the island's oldest building, dating from the sixties, a warehouse constructed of bricks said to have come around the Horn as ballast in sailing ships. It was part of Camp Reynolds, the first post on the island; the overgrown remnants of the camp occupy the sloping hillside to the rear. The camp's hospital was built in a more sheltered spot on the north side of the island. "Hospital Cove," as it came to be called, was the place where Ayala had landed nearly a century before. In the sixties, as a result of unfounded "buried treasure" rumors, the cove's beach was pocked with holes left by treasure seekers.

For half a century many travelers who had entered the Golden Gate on ships from across the Pacific had occasion to remember Angel Island with a shudder. Hospital Cove was the site of the U. S. Quarantine Station from 1892 until the end of World War II. In the early days passengers from "contaminated" vessels were herded through fumigation tanks; their clothes were passed through a steam bath which left them clean but often colorless.

Even more unsavory in reputation was the Immigration Station, which was built on the northwest corner near Point Simpton in 1908 and became the Pacific counterpart of New York's Ellis Island. Critics charged that the buildings were firetraps and that the immigrants, particularly Orientals, were badly abused. Although European immigrants were lodged individually in good-sized quarters while awaiting formalities, the Orientals, including Chinese "picture brides," were jammed by the hundreds into open barracks and sometimes held indefinitely at the pleasure of the authorities. The buildings still stand, now hidden like the old Army structures by rampant foliage.

The island's plant life is not only phenomenally aggressive when left to its own devices but has frequently seemed to inspire visitors to botanical efforts of their own. Most of the exotic vegetation at Hospital Cove was planted by early-day visitors, perhaps by sea captains returning from Asia with plant specimens or even by temporary Asiatic residents of the Immigration Station. Towering above Fort McDowell are sequoias set out many years ago by conservation groups, and in spring the hills are aglow with wild flowers, which in part owe their existence to the members of the San Francisco Wildflower Society who sowed tons of seed there in the 1920s. The animal population, though not as prolific as the plant life, is still large, including seals, raccoons, otters, deer, and some eighty varieties of birds.

Journey into Time   "Angel Island Day" has been celebrated twice by bay area residents. After World War II the Army had moved out and planted a "for sale" sign on its insular real estate. Groups interested in making the island a park sponsored open-house festivities in 1949 and again in 1952, and fifteen to twenty thousand curious people were ferried across for the two Sunday outings. The visitors explored the beach where Dana had landed; the dueling ground where Johnson and Ferguson fought their reluctant encounter; "Alcatraz Gardens," a high plateau on the southwest side, where vegetables were once raised for the mess tables of Alcatraz; secluded Hermit's Dell, where a recluse named Peter Casey lived in the sixties; the shell-mound remains of Indian villages; the excavations near Quarry Point, where Angel Island bluestone was mined for use in the construction of some of San Francisco's imposing pre-earthquake buildings; the trails through chaparral-covered hillsides and groves of oak, pine, laurel, and eucalyptus.

After the 1952 fête the voters of San Francisco enthusiastically approved a proposal that the city annex the island as a park. While the purchase boggled for years in red tape, there was a change of heart in Washington. Angel Island seemed a good site for a base for the new Nike guided missiles to protect the bay area from invading aircraft. The Army moved back, reactivating part of Fort McDowell. The top of Mount Ida, the island's peak, was flattened for radar purposes, and large areas on the southeast side were excavated for rocket-launching sites.

But the park enthusiasts won a consolation prize. The State Park Commission took over the Hospital Cove area, planned to rename it, appropriately, Ayala Cove, and to open it to the public. There was also the possibility that the Army might relinquish other areas, making most of the island available for park purposes.

A more ideal park site would be hard to find, for a trip to Angel Island is a brief journey across the water and a long journey back into time—an opportunity to observe what the bay shores were like before the white men came and in some of the eras since, a chance to peer out of our own cranny of the present into the long past and to sense the aura of timelessness which hovers about the island like vagrant wisps of a summer fog.

BELVEDERE—ISLAND OR PENINSULA?

Whether Belvedere is an island—or ever was—has long been debated, and at one point the issue was the subject of bitter litigation. Early Marin residents neatly dodged the issue by calling it "Peninsular Island." On most of the early maps its mile-long ridge is shown as connected with Tiburon Peninsula by a sandspit near the north end.

In the 1860s a squatter named Kershaw settled on the ridge's slopes, raised goats, planted fruit trees, and planned to develop "Kershaw's Island" as a hunting and fishing resort. But heirs of John Read, Marin pioneer and owner of Rancho Corte Madera del Presidio, which included most of the southeast part of the county, maintained that the place was legally part of the rancho and that Kershaw was trespassing. The squatter retorted that it could not possibly belong to the rancho since it was an island, and islands were not included in the original grant.

What happened next belongs to legend. According to one story, Kershaw dug a shallow channel through the spit, severing the connection with the mainland, to substantiate his claim that the place was an island. But the enterprising promoter thereby almost outsmarted himself. U.S. agents got wind of the dispute and declared that if the place was really an island it legally belonged to the government.

Kershaw did some fast thinking. He had nothing to hide from the government, he said, and even invited the agents to come over, have dinner, and see for themselves. Carefully he studied the tide tables, discovered a day and time when there was to be a particularly low tide, and extended his invitation for that precise hour.

The story goes that his guests arrived on time, and he escorted them personally across the spit when it was high and dry. Then, before the tide came in, he hustled them off to other parts of the island and poured the liquor freely until the tide went out again. Crossing back to Tiburon on dry land, the agents were convinced that Kershaw's Island was really a peninsula and not within their jurisdiction.

Kershaw's ruse—if indeed it ever took place—was only temporarily successful. Eventually the government learned that its agents had been outwitted and sent somebody over to check at high tide. The squatter was summarily evicted; and a contingent of soldiers camped on the "island" and planted the Stars and Stripes at its peak.

But the Read heirs were not yet to be counted out. They protested strongly and took the case to court. After a lengthy battle the disputed area was declared to be not a natural island but a peninsula and thus part of the rancho. It was purchased from the Read heirs by a real estate company in 1888, renamed Belvedere, and developed into the most beautiful— and highest-priced—residential area on the bay's shores.

Even while it was still "Kershaw's Island," it was a yachtsmen's headquarters, and its San Francisco Yacht Club, founded just two decades after the beginning of the Gold Rush, is the oldest in California. Once yachts were moored in the lagoon between Belvedere and Tiburon for protection during the winter season, but the natural channel through the southern sandspit, spanned for a time by a drawbridge, was eventually filled in for a road. The lagoon was cut off and in 1950 was partly filled in as a residential development.

In the nineties and for several decades thereafter Belvedere Cove was an anchorage for about thirty houseboats or arks. Some were weekend retreats; some were full-time homes for the local bohemian set. A few were put on pilings along the north side of the southern spit and there remain, opposite a row of overwater houses which include the beached cabin of an abandoned ship.

On the western shore at the water's edge is part of an old cod fishery, where vessels from Alaska brought their catches for processing in the last years of the nineteenth century. The remains of the ancient building have been converted into rustic living quarters for artists and writers.

The fishery was Belvedere's first and last industrial establishment. Belvedere may not be a natural island but its inhabitants are determined to maintain its residential insularity against the rising tide of commercialism. Although it is an incorporated town of fifteen hundred, except in the filled lagoon area it has no sidewalks, no electric signs, and no stores. To shop, its residents must go to the "mainland."

Belvedere is Italian for "beautiful view," and the name was well chosen. The superb scenery is unsurpassed anywhere on the bay. Above cliffs rising sharply on three sides from the water's edge, pine- and eucalyptus-clad slopes taper back to a three-hundred-fifty-foot peak; landscaped estates command sweeping views of the Marin shore, towering Tamalpais, the Golden Gate, and San Francisco.

THE LESSER ISLES

The most colorful of the bay's lesser isles—in several different ways—is Red Rock, four miles north of Angel Island and just south of the Richmond-San Rafael Bridge. It was called Golden Rock in earlier times, when one of the bay's innumerable buried treasure legends was attached to it, but its natural ruddy hue—the result of iron oxides—won out over the legend and gave it its present name.

At one point the title was believed to be appropriate for reasons other than its color. During the trial of labor leader Tom Mooney for a 1916 parade bombing in San Francisco, a police inspector became convinced that Mooney had hidden quantities of dynamite on Red Rock for later use. The inspector combed the island but found no dynamite.

He did find, however, something that seemed of far greater value. He stumbled across the information that the rock contained deposits of manganese which had been partly mined in the 1870s and then forgotten. He filed a claim on the island and triumphantly announced to the newspapers that he had acquired a fortune in the valuable metal.

After spending considerable money tunneling through the rock, the inspector was sadly forced to admit that the manganese was almost as ephemeral as the dynamite. What ore the island possessed was not of commercial grade, and he regretfully abandoned the rock to the elements. Red Rock has been useful from another aspect, however. Its position makes it a convenient boundary corner for three counties—Marin, Contra Costa, and San Francisco.

Among the bay's scattered smaller rocks is a family group —The Brothers, two islets off Point San Pablo, one occupied by a lighthouse, and The Sisters, a similar pair off Point San

Pedro opposite. A large white buoy off Telegraph Hill marks the site of submerged Blossom Rock, which provided early-day San Francisco with one of its greatest spectacles when in 1870 it was sheared off (as a menace to navigation) in a gigantic explosion. A similar show took place some thirty years later when Arch Rock, a mile west of Alcatraz, was blown up for the same reason.

The two small Marin Islands off San Rafael, from which the county took its name, were once the home of a Lacatuit tribe led by "Chief" Marin, the wily fighter and later ferryman. On the larger island buckeye trees planted in rows (the Indians used buckeye flower to make meal) and typical Indian shell mounds seem to indicate that the place had been the habitation of Marin's ancestors for many centuries. The chief's successor as monarch of the Marin Islands is Thomas Crowley, Sr., owner of many of the bay's tugboats. He bought the islands from the government in 1922 and built a summer home on the larger of the two, leaving the smaller one to the resident egret colony.

The biggest of the bay's lesser isles is Brooks Island, four times the size of Alcatraz yet unknown to most bay area residents. It has little claim to distinction, however, being simply a barren hill rising one hundred fifty feet out of the bay a half mile off Richmond. It has at various times been the site of a sheep pasture, a quarry, an orchard, a piggery, and a shrimp camp.

The bay has one migrating island. Just north of the Bay Bridge toll plaza are several acres of piled-up bay bottom dredged from the Oakland Outer Harbor in 1927, called, appropriately, Sand Island. During its first two decades currents and winds from the Golden Gate transported sand from the windward side to the leeward, causing the island to move fifty yards closer to shore.

Over the water around the edges of the island are shacks

and blinds built by duck hunters. The island itself was for many years a hobo jungle where the men of the road, who had access via a catwalk from the toll plaza, lived in shanties constructed from crates and other debris washed up on the shore.

In 1953 the island was leased from the Port of Oakland by radio station KROW as a new site for its transmitter, and the hobo jungle was removed by bulldozer in order to install ground wires. So effective a conductor was the water-soaked sand that KROW's signal was immediately doubled in strength.

As a man-made island, however, this piece of mid-bay territory takes strictly second billing to its far larger neighbor three miles west.

CITY OF LIGHT

On Treasure Island the future is past.

The future was a city that rose from the waters of the bay, shone briefly like a vision in the night, then disappeared forever.

The creation of the island was the result of two ideas that were causing a stir in San Francisco in the early 1930s: one the plan for a close-in San Francisco airport and the other the proposal for an exposition to celebrate the completion of the bay's two great bridges.

Both the backers of the airport and those of the fair were looking for a good location. Somebody remembered that the Central Pacific Railroad, sixty years earlier, had planned to establish its headquarters in the bay by filling in the shoals north of Yerba Buena. With the Bay Bridge scheduled to bring Yerba Buena within ten minutes' driving distance of the

city, what better site for a fair—and an airport to be built
there when the fair was over? The fair and airport people
merged forces, obtained financial help from Washington, and
went to work.

Pacifica   Engineers first dumped thousands of tons of rock
into the bay, enclosing the shoals with a wall thirteen feet
above sea level. Into the enclosure—a mile long and two thirds
of a mile wide—they poured twenty million cubic yards of
mud from the adjacent bay bottom to create the new island
and connected it with a ramp roadway to Yerba Buena and
the bridge.

Then they had to "unsalt" the mud—drain the bay water
out so that the soil would support vegetation. They drilled
two hundred wells on the soggy island and pumped them
dry. Rains washed out more salt. And as a final precaution
eighty thousand cubic yards of rich peat topsoil were barged
in from the islands of the delta and spread across the surface
for garden areas.

Meanwhile San Francisco was planning to tell the world
about its forthcoming big show. With a world's fair scheduled
in New York for the same year (it has never been satisfacto-
rily determined which fair was scheduled first) San Francisco
would have to beat the drums loudly in bidding for visitors.

The new island would need a name. One publicity man
had an inspiration: the island was made from bay bottom
carpeted with silt which had been washed down from the
river, much of it during the gold era; the soil of the island
must surely contain particles of gold from the Mother Lode!

"Gold Island" didn't sound right. But "Treasure Island"
was a natural. Appropriately costumed "miners" were photographed panning "gold" from the soil of Treasure Island.

Meanwhile Leland Cutler, the fair's general manager, was
engaged in more serious work. Since the theme of the fair was

to be the cultures of the Pacific, he made a tour of the capitals of Asia and persuaded twenty-one nations to send major exhibits. China was too busy with the invading Japanese to be concerned with expositions, so the residents of San Francisco's Chinatown raised a million dollars to construct a Chinese village on the island—at a safe and suitable distance from the Japanese exhibit.

The engineers and architects were overcoming formidable obstacles. The island was in the direct path of the prevailing summer winds from the Golden Gate; for protection, a wall nearly as high as a ten-story building was constructed along the entire windward side of the island. The filled-in land was still settling when the buildings were begun, so they were constructed in a special cantilever fashion with "hanging" walls, unsusceptible to damage from continued settling.

When it was finished, early in 1939, the fair was a feast for the eyes. The architecture of its principal buildings and courts was a surprisingly harmonious combination of Pacific styles; themes of the Americas were blended with those of Southern Asia. Visitors arriving by ferry walked through the great Aztec-Inca "elephant gates" to the broad Court of Honor, dominated by the four-hundred-foot Tower of the Sun. So loftily did the tower rise above the rest of the fairgrounds that on one occasion a visitor looking straight up from near its base saw wisps of fog flying swiftly past its top, had the illusion that the tower was falling, and yelled a frightened alarm that scattered visitors in all directions.

The other dominating feature of the fair was the seventy-foot theme statue, *Pacifica*, the figure of a woman with her hands raised in benediction, symbolizing peace among the nations around the rim of the ocean. In the four main courts were long arrays of fountains, sculpture, flowers, bas-reliefs, and murals symbolizing the meeting of Pacific cultures.

At night the exposition was flooded with contrasting pastel

lights that shone not only on the buildings and courts but on the pools and falling waters. As seen from San Francisco, with the fair's illuminated domes and towers reflected in the dark waters of the bay, Treasure Island seemed an image of some mythical city of light conjured in the brain of a poet—Tennyson's Palace of Art or the Pleasure Dome of Kubla Khan.

"T.I."   Like the competing fair in New York, the San Francisco exposition was not financially profitable. Its ultimate value was necessarily measured in other terms. The great expositions of the past were notable not for any immediate returns but for their impact on the minds of their visitors. The Philadelphia Centennial of 1876, featuring such technological innovations as the Corliss engine, stimulated men's imaginations with the possibilities of industrialism. The Eiffel Tower, constructed for the Paris Exposition of 1889, was the precursor of the modern skyscraper city. The San Francisco exposition, too, in its central theme, was a prophecy of things to come—the meeting of the arts and sciences of the Pacific, the merging of Western industrialism with the ancient cultures of Asia and the Indo-European culture of Latin America. The exposition was a look westward into the future.

There is no doubt that it was ahead of its time. Within a few months after it opened World War II was under way in Europe. Before it closed, Paris had fallen to Hitler. Six weeks after Pearl Harbor, the figure of Pacifica, symbol of peace, undermined by the wreckers' dynamite, came tumbling down.

San Francisco granted the island to the Navy for emergency use and decided to center all its airport operations at the peninsula site. The exposition buildings were soon swarming with blue-clad sailors en route to the Far East. The Hall of Western States was converted into a barracks; the old river boat *Delta Queen*, which had ferried visitors to the exposition, was used for quarters and classrooms; the Food and Beverages Building became "the world's biggest mess hall," serving seven thousand meals an hour.

At the war's end the pipe line was reversed, and "T.I."—as the sailors called it—became the first U.S. stop on the homeward trip for hundreds of thousands of returning Navy men. At the maximum it processed twelve thousand naval personnel a day. After the war the Navy acquired the island on a permanent basis, housing four commands: the Naval Receiving Station, processing Pacific-bound personnel; a Naval Schools Command; the Naval Station, administering the island itself; and the headquarters of the Western Sea Frontier. The exposition's three permanent buildings, at the south end of the island, are still in use by the Navy.

In the center of the island is a large enclosure of tile and marble surrounded by statuary—the Fountain of Western Waters, which once cascaded before the giant statue of Pacifica. Hurrying sailors, many of whom were babes in arms when these waters flowed last, stare curiously at it as if it were the remains of some former civilization.

But it is not the past at which they gaze. It is the day after tomorrow.

ISLAND OF LEGENDS

Yerba Buena probably has the largest transient population of any island in the world. Its transients, moreover, spend most of their time there underground. The duration of their stay averages less than one minute as they hurtle in cars or trains or busses through the tunnel which pierces the island's middle, connecting the two sections of the Bay Bridge.

To most of the commuters who whisk twice daily through

the double-decked tunnel Yerba Buena is scarcely an island at all but simply the hub of the cross-bay transportation system and has none of the glamour attached to its insular neighbors in the bay. Actually, however, in one sense it is the most glamorous of all; it has more legends connected with it than have all the bay's other islands together. Even if only a fraction of the wealth reputed to have been buried there is intact, Yerba Buena, far more than its adjacent neighbor, deserves the name Treasure Island, and its residents should hardly be able to step out the back door without stumbling over doubloons and pieces of eight.

The Lost Treasure of Mission Dolores   One of the island's earliest legends arose out of the Mexican Government's secularization of the California missions in 1833. The padres at San Francisco's Mission Dolores hastily packed the altar cloths, silver implements, gold, and jewels into chests and put them aboard a sloop for shipment to Spain.

The vessel had scarcely left its anchorage, according to the tale, when a severe storm struck, nearly swamped the craft, and finally piled it up on the north shore of Yerba Buena. Although some lives were lost, the treasure was kept intact and buried on the island for safekeeping.

Suspicion arose that some members of the crew had wrecked the vessel purposely in order to seize the mission's wealth, but it may be that the plotters themselves were the ones who were drowned in the attempt. At any rate there is no record that the treasure was recovered, and presumably it still safely rests in its legendary hiding place.

From that time on the treasure buriers came to the island in such a steady stream that it seems remarkable they did not spade up each other's jewels. The next treasure tale took place shortly after the mission treasure was buried. An American whaling ship, making its way around the Horn en route to the North Pacific, stopped at the port of Callao on the coast of Peru to take on water and found one of the customary revolutions in progress. Members of the embattled wealthy class pleaded with the captain of the vessel to take their valuables on board for safety reasons until the revolution was quelled.

The captain obligingly took two barrels of coin and a large casket of jewels. The revolutionists continued to hold the upper hand, however, and the American skipper, according to his story, grew tired of waiting. Impatiently he hoisted anchor and headed north, intending to stop again on his way back. Putting in at San Francisco Bay, he decided to deposit the treasure until his return from the arctic whaling grounds.

One dark night the skipper chose two of his crew, swore them to secrecy, and set out in a small boat for one of the bay's islands, where they stashed away the Peruvian loot. One of the two crewmen, however, a native of the West Indies named Charles Stewart, jumped ship and remained in the bay area.

The vessel never returned from the arctic. Although the island in question was popularly supposed to have been Yerba Buena, Stewart, who enjoyed retelling the tale, never revealed the exact hiding place. He maintained that as a man of honor he could not be expected to violate his oath.

A number of other buried treasures on Yerba Buena did not remain buried for long. During the 1830s and '40s, for example, the tangled thickets on the island's slopes were supposedly used by smugglers as a temporary repository for opium and other oriental contraband, where it remained until it could safely be picked up by agents ashore. And in one of the devastating fires which swept shanty-built San Francisco during the Gold Rush looters reportedly made off with large quantities of the yellow metal and buried it on Yerba Buena, but most of it was eventually recovered by police.

Among the island's other legends of treasure one has a particularly imaginative twist. As told by historian Robert O'Brien, it took place in the 1870s, when spiritualism was in vogue, and there were a number of practitioners of the art in San Francisco who claimed to be making regular contact with the Great Beyond. Strangely, several of them had received communications from one Don Abecco Monte Janeiro, the ghost of a pirate who had preyed on the Manila galleons which had sailed down the coast before California was settled. The buccaneer's shade told the mediums that he had buried some $20,000,000 worth of Spanish doubloons on Yerba Buena.

Logically the spiritualists decided to pool their resources and hunt the treasure together. As might be expected, however, they had a quarrel as to how the anticipated spoils would be divided and split into two factions. In order to get the jump on the rival faction, one party rowed to the island at night, made their calculations, paced off the distances, and began to dig. As they did so, out of a fringe of woods in the darkness appeared the ghostly figure of a pirate—presumably Don Abecco—who waved a cutlass at them and howled ferociously. Rocks were showered on them as they fled in terror to their boat.

Later they learned that the rival party of spiritualists had been on the island that same night, and it dawned on them that they had been hoaxed. Neither party found old Don Abecco's $20,000,000, however. The reason was volunteered by yet another medium to whom the ghost of the pirate appeared and confided that his treasure was still well hidden.

"Since it was buried," he whispered from the Beyond, "the earth has shaken many times, and now it is deeper and the rock has closed over it." He concluded enigmatically: "Under what appears to be a rock on the island are pools no man may fathom."

Workmen digging the Bay Bridge tunnel evidently failed to disturb the hiding place. And it is not inconceivable that on windy nights old Don Abecco still patrols the island, appearing only as a flicker of moonlight among the trees in the secluded dells far above the tunnel's speeding traffic.

Goat Island   Replete with legendary treasures, Yerba Buena has also been generously endowed with names, having had at various times more titles than all the bay's other major islands together. When Captain Beechey in 1826 erroneously transferred Ayala's name "Isla de Alcatraces" to the present Alcatraz on his map, he labeled this island Yerba Buena for the "good herb" or wild mint, a fragrant creeper then growing prolifically on the bay's shores and used by the Spanish to flavor their tea.

The Americans, who preferred something snappier in the way of names, took to calling it Wood Island or Bird Island. The name that stuck longest, however, was derived from the herds of goats which were pastured there by early settlers and which rapidly multiplied until there were hundreds swarming the isle when the forty-niners arrived. Although most of the inhabitants of "Goat Island" were soon devoured by meat-hungry Argonauts, the last of the animals, an ancient but tough survivor named Lonesome Billy, ruled the island around the turn of the century. The name outlasted even Billy, however, and the government map makers eventually yielded to popular usage and erased "Yerba Buena" for "Goat Island."

That name stuck until 1931, when the U. S. Geographic Board finally surrendered to a fifteen-year crusade led by historian Nellie van de Grift Sanchez, broke all precedent by reversing itself, and officially redesignated the island Yerba Buena. Diehard old-timers still defiantly cling to the earthier name, however.

The Indians had a fishing station and temescal—sweat house—on the island and used the cove on the southeast side as a burial ground. Archaeologists unearthed a skull there which had an abalone shell fastened in the mouth in such a position that it may have been used for holding the tongue— a fact which caused an early historian to speculate that the skull was undoubtedly that of a woman and that the Indians had apparently been more ingenious than they had been given credit for.

During the decade after the discovery of gold the island was occupied by a settler named Thomas Dowling, who built a house at the cove near the old burial ground and developed a sandstone quarry nearby. In order to discourage San Francisco excursionists from swarming over his property he turned loose on the island a bad-tempered bull, which soon acquired a reputation as an unwelcome guest at island picnics. To the grim satisfaction of the picnickers, the bull eventually became a menace even to Dowling and his family and had to be eliminated, giving his pursuers a bad time among the island's dense growth before he was finally cornered and shot.

Doubtless the picnickers had further cause for gloating when in 1866 the U. S. Government evicted Dowling and made the island an Army post.

Political Prize   Yerba Buena became the pawn in a hard-fought political hassel in 1869 when the builders of the Central Pacific proposed to take over the island, level it, fill in the adjoining shoals, build a causeway to Oakland, and make the island the western terminal of the transcontinental railroad.

Prompted by Leland Stanford and other owners of the railroad, the state legislature obediently agreed to grant the Central Pacific the shoals north of Yerba Buena and a two-hundred-fifty-foot strip to the mainland; and a bill was introduced in Congress to hand over the island itself to the railroad.

Anxious San Franciscans suspected that the Central Pacific, which was already imperiously throwing its weight around California, would set itself up on a railroad-owned industrial city in mid-bay, make it the hub of the bay area economy, and leave San Francisco a by-passed suburb. The Chamber of Commerce fought the proposal doggedly and sent a high-powered committee to Washington. The railroad's logical Western terminal, the committee insisted, was San Francisco itself, and the city offered to build a transbay railroad crossing in the shallows of the bay twenty miles to the south to bring the rails over.

The delegation achieved a Pyrrhic victory. Congress refused to release Yerba Buena, but the railroad proceeded to build its terminal in Oakland, leaving San Francisco permanently without direct transcontinental rail service.

A more aesthetic plan for the island was suggested in 1886 by California poet Joaquin Miller. He proposed to reforest Yerba Buena, which like Angel Island had been denuded by early-day wood gatherers. Although Miller had some poetically impractical notions about the effects of a tree belt on the island (he claimed that it would "break the force of the densest fog"), the idea caught on, and the result was California's first Arbor Day. Thousands of school children swarmed over Yerba Buena at the designated hour, planting the trees in the form of a Greek cross stretching the length and breadth of the island, according to the poet's plan. Unfortunately most of the trees perished in a subsequent fire, but more plantings took place later, and the present Monterey pine and eucalyptus groves on the upper slopes undoubtedly owe their existence to Miller's arboreal enterprise.

The Army had meanwhile lost interest in the island, and in 1898 the Navy moved in, set up a training station, and later replaced it by a receiving center. The latter was transferred to Treasure Island at the beginning of World War II, and Yerba Buena has since become a residential suburb of its man-made neighbor. Accommodations range from barracks and a guardhouse to the big landscaped estate of the commander of the Western Sea Frontier on the north slopes. On the island's peak is an abandoned observation tower formerly used to signal naval vessels in the bay. The old lighthouse on the southwest corner is maintained by the Coast Guard, and on the site of the Indian cemetery and the Dowling house in the cove to the east is a Coast Guard depot which maintains all aids to navigation in Northern California, including buoys, lighthouses, and lightships.

Like many of the bay's islands, Yerba Buena reflects great contrasts and sharp paradoxes. For the commuter, time on the island is condensed into the few seconds it takes him to traverse the tunnel. He is propelled through the island's interior more than one hundred years distant from the wooded slopes and grassy glades above, where the roar of traffic through the tunnel is no louder than the sound of a far-off surf, and the tread of the ghosts is almost audible—ghosts of Indians from the ancient burial ground, of padres and pirates, of treasure planters and gold seekers from a leisurely, legend-spinning past when the imagination had ample time to indulge its penchant for island adventure.

DAY'S END

All day a moving cloud canopy has hung over the gray bay, occasionally trailing long banners of rain which stippled the waters and gently sprinkled the shores. Now, at day's end, comes a violent transformation. The sun has descended beneath the western edge of the canopy and floods the bay and its shores with light.

The bridge at the narrows is black against the sun, and in the sky beyond it are long glowing bars of cloud strata, radiating feathery banners of flame. The water surface, the misty air, and the clouds are suffused with golden opalescence. Again, as in early spring, the cities climbing the East Bay hills are ablaze with the reflected light of the western sky.

A radiant bank of cumulus over Angel Island is mirrored in the calm bay. An outward-bound ship, gold in the sun, is reflected in the blue-gold waters and leaves a dark, spreading wake across the surface. A pink wreath of fog moves over a ridge behind Sausalito. Over the ocean a plane climbs high like an insect drawn into the caldron of light. The bay alternately glows and fades beneath the changing sky as clouds laden with fire pass overhead.

In a few minutes' time the golds and pinks in sky and water are replaced by crimson, changing to purple and to gray. Quickly the sky darkens, and the spectacle vanishes as suddenly as it came.

12

Tides in the Sky

There is nothing on earth exactly like the fog of San Francisco Bay. None of the thousand evanescent forms of air and water that move across the globe between the equator and the poles is as fantastic in shape and motion yet as tangible and intimate as the thick white vapor that rolls through the Golden Gate in summertime like an air-borne flood and spreads to the farthest reaches of the bay and its shores.

In most parts of the earth, fog traditionally is a dark, disagreeable smudge that comes from nowhere, hides the sun, obscures the vision, afflicts the lungs, and casts a damp pall over the land. In San Francisco the fog is a thing of beauty and wonder, a daily drama of the elements with the wide bay itself as the central stage.

It is a thing of mystery, too—the mystery of imagined happenings, the suspected drama of half-seen comings and goings, of ships and shadows and men moving like ghosts in the billows. It is the mystery of a phantom element that rises from the surrounding waters and brings directly to the eyes, ears, faces, and lungs of hurried city dwellers an immediate symbol of the greater mysteries beyond—the rolling sea and the turning earth and the ocean of air overhead.

For the San Francisco fog, like the bay itself, is born of the violent meeting of land and sea at the place where the ocean has breached the western mountain barrier and invaded the continent's edge. It is conceived out of the cold oceanic deeps and the fertile heat of the Central Valley. It is shaped and given substance by the rotations of the planet and the drift of the currents and the flowing of the rivers of atmosphere.

Upwelling Waters   At winter's end the spring sun, climbing farther north each day over the North American Continent, brings welcome warmth to the land. It heats the deserts of the Southwest and spreads a mantle of green through the fields and forests of the Great Plains. It melts the snows of the Appalachians, the Rockies, and the Sierra Nevada, and sends rivers running full to the sea.

Slowly, through March and April and into May, the warming air over the land expands and rises; the weight of the atmosphere diminishes; and on the walls of weather bureaus across the continent thermometers rise and barometers fall perceptibly day by day.

A thousand miles west of the continent's edge, however, the heaving blue waters of the Pacific respond far more slowly to the northward advance of the sun, and the air over the ocean remains wintry long after the continent has begun to warm. The cool, heavy air hugs the rolling surface and presses down on the water. On ships from the California coast to the China Sea barometers remain high.

Warming air and low pressure over the land; cool air and

high pressure over the sea—an inequality which nature will never tolerate for long. A major change in the balance of forces is in the offing.

The low cool air over the ocean begins to move landward to replace the rising warm air over the continent, slowly at first, then gaining momentum until it attains the proportions of a wind. But in its headlong rush to the land it is deflected by a strong sideward force, set up by the rotation of the earth beneath it. Like a person walking on a merry-go-round, the wind begins to veer to the right. The same impulse that causes the water to circle to the right in a bathtub drain anywhere in the Northern Hemisphere—and in the bay itself (scientists call it the "Coriolis force")—affects the landward-rushing winds of the Pacific. By the time they reach the beaches of California, they are moving not from due west but from the northwest, almost paralleling the slanting coastline.

The cool ocean winds are blocked in their attempt to move onto the warm land not only by their natural tendency to veer to the right but by the Coast Range, the mountain wall along the western rim of the continent, which further deflects them southward.

And so from March or April until early September the prevailing northwest winds whip down the California coast, bending the coastal cypresses and laurels into permanently contorted shapes and sending the waves smashing into sheets of spray on headland after headland, from Trinidad Head in the north to Cape Mendocino to Point Bonita and south all the way to Point Conception above Santa Barbara, where the coast turns sharply east. The rushing masses of air are so persistent and powerful that they are able to move even the surface of the sea itself. Driven before the spring and summer winds, the ocean surface runs south in a coastwise current one hundred miles wide.

The turning of the earth affects not only the winds but

everything that moves freely on its surface. Water, too, is subject to the same rightward drift that deflects the moving air, and the current running down the coast continually veers offshore. As the masses of water move away from the coastline, they tend to leave a vacuum; from somewhere must come more water to take their place. It comes from the only possible direction—straight down.

The result is an overturn, an upwelling of bottom water from the continental shelf. From sunless depths several hundred to a thousand feet below the surface, water "boils" to the top, bringing a bottom layer auguring well for fishermen but ill for swimmers. It is full of rich minerals nourishing to oceanic plants and fish, but its temperature is in the mid-fifties—ten to fifteen degrees colder than the water beyond the zone of upwelling and the coldest water to be found in summer on any coast of the United States.

When the spring upwelling begins along the six hundred miles of California coast from St. George Reef near the Oregon border to Point Conception, the scene is set for the transmutation of elements which creates the fog.

War in the Air   An ocean breeze off Cape Mendocino, laden with moisture and warmed by the spring sun during its long arc over the Pacific, strikes icy water which has welled up from the bottom nine hundred feet below. The air is cooled. As happens whenever warm, moist air strikes a cold surface—a windowpane, for example, or a glass of water —its moisture is condensed. At the same instant the same breeze scuffs the ocean beneath it into a ruffle of foam, flinging salt spray above the surface. As the ocean water falls back, the particles of salt remain in the air. Around a single air-borne salt particle a globule of the condensed water forms, large enough to be visible, small enough to float in mid-air.

Millions of other salt particles are similarly flying into the air and forming nuclei for drops of water condensed from the cooled wind. Inch by inch, mile by mile, as the wind blows over the cold surface, the droplets of water continue to form, creating first a hazy vapor, then a cloud on the water. The great summer fogs of the California coast have come into being.

At the maximum the thick vapor forms a continuous bank perhaps a hundred miles wide, hundreds of feet high, and more than six hundred miles long. Slowly the white mass grows, rolls inland with the wind, charges up coastal canyons in phalanx. Big drops of it congregate on the leaves of low-growing ferns and towering redwoods, drip to the ground and keep damp the roots of the ancient trees that have depended on this nourishment for thousands of years.

On a summer afternoon drive toward San Francisco from the south over the Skyline Boulevard on the crest of the peninsula. Look down to the left on the top of the fog as the surging tide rolls through the redwood canyons, glaring white in the afternoon sun, ridged and furrowed from molding itself to the shapes of the hills beneath it. It seems to pound the high mountain ridges like a gargantuan slow-motion surf, rebounding from unyielding peaks in high looping curves, sending vapory spray hundreds of feet into the air, pouring voluminously through gaps and saddles, surrounding high ridges which loom like islands in the vapor, washing against the summit peaks which remain aloof in the warm dry air above.

It is as if the ocean, impatient with the ponderous slowness of its own sea-level war on the cliffs at the continent's edge, were sending its aerial armadas to carry the attack inland. Along most of the six-hundred-mile front the fog is rebuffed by the coastal mountain wall. But at the Golden Gate, the one point in the coastline where the ocean itself has already breached the continental defenses, its air troops pour through with massive force, fanning out over the bay as if to exploit to the fullest the break-through in the enemy lines.

Thus in the air as well as in the water the bay area is a main arena of battle between the elements. The gigantic land-sea conflict that gave birth to the bay is paralleled not only in the daily struggles between the flood and ebb of the bay itself but in the summer-long battle between the tides of the air as well.

The inner stronghold of the forces of the land is the Central Valley. The summer sun beats down on the mountain-enclosed basin with unabated intensity, creating an ovenlike dry heat that grows immense quantities of fruits and vegetables, cotton and grains. From Bakersfield to Fresno to Chico to Red Bluff temperatures often soar far above 100°. Unlike the Mississippi Valley, which is invaded by moist air from the Gulf of Mexico, creating summer thunderheads and cool showers, the Central Valley of California is too dry to produce summer rains. It can be cooled only by another process: the rushing of the sea air through the only break in the valley's thousand-mile mountain perimeter—San Francisco Bay.

So the war between the elements rages; the ocean sends its fog-bearing winds through the gap in the mountains to drive back the warm dry air and take possession of the land; the land air strikes back at the fog with withering blasts from the hot valley. And the ocean retaliates in force: The hotter the valley, the swifter the sea winds, the thicker the fog on the bay.

As in most evenly matched contests, the tide of battle flows back and forth with cyclical regularity. There is a daily cycle; the fog moves in over the bay in the afternoon, makes its greatest penetration at night, then retreats as the land air, heated by the morning sun, counterattacks in strength.

There is a longer cycle, lasting from about three days to several weeks; its average length is about a week, however, and it can thus be termed a weekly cycle. Each night the fog penetrates a little farther than the night before and is driven back a shorter distance in the morning. Finally it reaches the Central Valley, becomes overextended and disappears. The bay then has clear weather for a few days until the weekly cycle begins again.

And there is a seasonal cycle; from May to August, as the Central Valley heat increases and the sea winds through the Golden Gate grow to full strength, the hours of fog per day in San Francisco gradually increase. Then the winds and fogs begin to wane and the sun is seen more often until October, when the fog season ends.

The Spectacle at the Gate   The forms of the ocean's aerial attack are infinite in number. Seldom is the battle line the same on two successive days. Depending on varying conditions of the winds, the currents, the upwelling, the air pressure, and the valley heat, the fog mass pouring through the Gate will alter its shape and course.

Early in the seasonal cycle before the winds are strong and before the upwelling has started in earnest (or late in September when the cold currents are weakening) a long finger of fog slips in through the Golden Gate just over the water, sometimes beneath the deck of the bridge; motorists drive above the vapor as if they were in a plane above a layer of clouds. It snakes in a long thin line to Alcatraz, rolls up and over the Rock like a breaking wave, and continues out over the bay until it evaporates.

At such times the fog's penetration may be directly affected by the tidal currents pouring through the Golden Gate. The wispy finger of vapor may extend far into the bay on the incoming tide when the cold ocean currents help to cool the surface air; it may evaporate entirely at the changing of the tide, when the sea waters beneath it are replaced by the sun-heated waters of the ebbing bay and the river, only to return again on the following flood tide. It is as if the air-borne invading force were dependent for support on the "ground" troops beneath it.

By late afternoon the fog may spread across the bay to Berkeley, hit the barrier of Grizzly Peak behind, and mushroom out along the Berkeley Hills in both directions, enclosing parts of Richmond and Oakland while downtown San Francisco is still enjoying the sun.

The most spectacular show put on by the fog takes place at the narrows of the Golden Gate. For a close view drive to Vista Point, overlooking the bay just north of the bridge. Go there at the beginning of a weekly fog cycle—about noon on a summer day when the vapor makes its first appearance after a several-day absence.

There you command a view comparable to that from the lookout point at the brink of Niagara. Standing in the sun, you face a river of fog that may be a mile wide and hundreds of feet deep. Here the funneled winds whip through the narrow strait with accelerated speed and turbulence, and the fog, which elsewhere moves in at a rate of ten to twenty miles per hour, here seems to double its pace. In the course of an hour, a million tons of water vapor will float past in front of you to the accompaniment of a foghorn chorus.

Most of the bridge is obscured. Streams of southbound automobiles move down the approach ramp, out onto the deck, and disappear in the moving vapors. The bright red top of the north tower rises above the fog river, appearing incredibly gigantic, detached as it is from all visible connection with land or sea. Occasionally, through the drifting vapors, the entire tower and the deck beneath it come into view. In front of it pass swiftly floating masses, banners, streamers, and swirling wisps that sift through the pattern of cables like billowing smoke.

To your right, just north of the span, seething vapors appear over the top of a ridge, boiling up from the windward side like steam from the nether regions. There the sudden change in the direction of the air currents creates a myriad of volatile fog shapes which shoot high into the sunlit air like foam from bursting breakers. Lower layers of the fog flow over the top of the ridge in intermittent streams, then fall slowly down the cliffside. Halfway down the slope swirls of the falling vapor leap out from the cliff, hit the bridge deck and the tops of moving cars, rebound in long curves over the east rail, then continue to plunge toward the bay, tumbling, eddying, and billowing like the spray of a mountain waterfall.

In more than appearance these falls in the rivers of the air are like the falls in the rivers of the land. Both are composed of descending water; both send out clouds of mist and spray; both are drawn irresistibly toward a specific destination—the land rivers to the ocean; the air rivers to the hot, low-pressure valleys of the interior.

Once past the narrows the separate fog shapes merge, as they move in over the bay, into a solid, vertical-sided mass of white, moving slowly eastward. On the bay's surface, sailboats take advantage of the accompanying winds, disappearing and reappearing as they tack in and out of the fog wall.

The sight from Vista Point is compelling, and the turbulent masses of vapor exert an almost hypnotic effect on the spectator. Of all the phenomena in nature that have a similar fascination—the leap of flames in an open fire, the rush and roar of a mountain stream, the rolling of breakers in an ocean surf—few take place on such a mammoth scale as this. Yet it is not the magnitude of the spectacle alone that entrances the beholder. Its spell lies partly in the sharp incongruity, the contrast between the angularity of this colossal monu-

ment of steel spanning the strait and the nebulous shapes
and motions of the rolling vapors that drift across it like vague
mysterious passages of music swirling around a central theme,
an intriguing counterpoint of reality and fantasy.

The Inversion   Like all aerial conflicts, the summertime
atmospheric war over the bay is waged not only horizontally
but vertically. The ocean air comes in low, displaces the expanding, rising land air, and forms a cooling, foggy blanket
over the bay's surface and its shores.

To feel at first hand the impact of the vertical warfare over
the bay area, climb Mount Tamalpais on a summer afternoon.
Even though the day may be fogless, about halfway up the
mountain the temperature of the air around you will suddenly within the space of a few feet rise ten to twenty degrees. You have climbed through the invisible barrier separating the cool sea air below and the warm land air above. You
have walked through the lid or ceiling of warm air that hangs
over the bay all summer, no matter how cool and foggy the
weather of the surface. Above the ceiling you stand in air that
previously lay in valleys around the bay sheltered from
ocean breezes, was heated by the sun, expanded, and rose to
this height as the marine air came in beneath it. When the fog
comes in, this ceiling is the level to which it will rise, held
there by the warm layer above it.

This condition—a layer of warm air above a layer of cool—
is called by meteorologists an "inversion," because in a sense
the atmosphere has been inverted; under more normal conditions warm air lies on the surface and cool air above.

Just as the ocean air and its fog push their way horizontally
into the Golden Gate and across the bay, causing the warm
land air to retreat, so they also push their way upward against
the inversion. At first the fog layer is only two or three hun-

dred feet deep, then, hour by hour, its top rises visibly higher as the layer thickens, forcing the ceiling upward.

The Golden Gate Bridge forms a perfect "thermometer" to gauge the height of the warm-air ceiling. At first the inversion may be as low as the 250-foot-high deck, then is pushed upward until the sea vapor envelops the tops of the 750-foot towers. This engulfment may occasionally occur all in one afternoon; more often it takes several days as each successive night the vapors push a little higher upward.

Simultaneously the fog is advancing horizontally over the bay and its shores. In San Francisco's seaside Sunset District the wall of vapor marches up the long slope from Ocean Beach on a broad front in early afternoon, sometimes preceeded by advance banners like low-flying clouds. The long white blocks of wall-to-wall houses are enveloped one by one. The thermometer drops several degrees. Housewives hurriedly gather in clothes on the line and swathe their children in sweaters.

When it reaches the high central spine of San Francisco from the Presidio to Mount Davidson, the fog will pause to gather strength. But there are gaps in the city's central ridge. Golden Gate Park lies in one of them, and on many a May afternoon the white tide from the sea comes rolling through the park's eucalyptus trees and across its lawns, lakes, and meadows, scattering the sun-bathers before it like Sunday papers in a sudden breeze.

Every afternoon and evening the fog rises a little higher. The city's heights and the valleys they protect may remain warm and sunlit much later in the season than the rest of the area, but ultimately, usually by early June at the latest, the oceanic forces are ready for the assault. In the Central Valley the sun is blazing down on fields and orchards from the Tehachapis in the south to Mount Shasta in the north; the warm surface air is rising; over the bay the cool ocean air is drawn valleyward with increasing force, bringing the fog with it.

Flags on San Francisco's high buildings stand stiffly eastward in the wind. Rising ocean vapors surmount the Presidio, Pacific Heights, Lone Mountain, and Mount Sutro, pushing upward against the inversion until the tops of the bridge towers are buried three hundred feet deep. Shoppers on Market Street look west, see the fog cresting Twin Peaks in a wave a hundred feet high and pouring down the near slopes in snowy cascades. Summer has come to the city.

The Bay's Canopy   Gradually, as the weekly and seasonal cycles advance and the wind and fog cool off the layers of air next to the ground, the fog-forming process is lifted into the air, and the entire layer of fog begins to rise. Not only does the top lift as it pushes against the inversion, but now the bottom, too, rises gradually from the water surface, forming a low ceiling over the bay which slants upward toward the east.

As the curtain of vapor lifts, fishing boats and ships become visible, and the foghorn concert ends. At the Golden Gate the bridge comes into sight from the bottom upward until the dark ceiling seems to rest on the tops of the towers.

Because of this progressive cooling of the lower layers of air, San Francisco's coldest days come not at the beginning of the weekly cycle, when the fog rolls through the streets, but some days later, when it hangs high overhead. At this point it forms a canopy Californians call a high fog. Tourists call it clouds. Both are correct. A cloud is a fog high in the air; a fog is a low cloud. But the tourist who wakes up in the morning, peers into dark skies, and expects rain will be happily disappointed. Methods of judging weather he may have developed in more normal climates fail utterly when applied to the bay area. Although at times the summer skies are grimly foreboding, particularly early in the morning, the vapor, held down by the inversion, never gets high enough to produce rain in the daytime. Occasionally at night the fog may be thick enough to produce a semi-drizzle which unknowing tourists may believe to be rain, but any native will solemnly inform him that such a thing is impossible—a heavy fog, but no rain.

By noon the overcast will probably burn off above most of the bay, although sometimes, at the high point of the weekly and seasonal cycles, you may not see the midsummer sun in San Francisco for days at a time. But sunshine is never far away. San Francisco is the coolest major city in the nation in summertime, but its location at the only gateway between the cool coast and the hot interior enables its residents to command a vast range of climates.

To get out from under the fog canopy, go ten or fifteen miles north to Mill Valley or San Anselmo, where you will be glad to seek the cool shade of the redwoods; or go south twenty-five miles to Redwood City or Palo Alto, sheltered by the peninsula hills, where the temperature may be twenty degrees higher. Go east across the bay and through the Broadway Tunnel into Contra Costa County behind the Berkeley Hills; at times you may encounter a thirty-degree difference in temperature from one end of the 3800-foot tunnel to the other.

Or if you really want it hot, keep going. Drive east another half hour into the Central Valley, where the mercury may stand above a hundred at times when the temperature at the fog-covered Golden Gate is in the low fifties—a temperature difference of fifty degrees in fifty miles.

Oddly, when the fog burns off in the heat of the morning sun, it dissipates not from the top but from the bottom. The sun's heat penetrates through the overcast and warms the earth's surface faster than it warms the thin air above the fog. And the earth radiates the heat back into the sky, melting off the lower layers of vapor first.

The initial breaking up comes around the fog's edges, farthest inland, and along the leeward slopes of hills where the ocean breeze is warmed as it descends. For this reason, the west side of the bay, in the lee of the coastal hills, is generally sunnier than the east shore, and San Francisco Airport is clear more often than Oakland Airport, just across the bay. In the days before instrument flying, incoming pilots trying to get below the ceiling to make a landing were advised by radio to look for holes in the fog behind Palo Alto and other areas along the base of the peninsula hills. Similarly, air-mail pilots heading for Crissy Field at the Presidio were directed to come down through clear spots in the lee of Tamalpais.

High Tide of Battle   The ebb and flow of the tides of fog follow patterns which are roughly comparable to the tidal patterns in the bay itself. Just as in the water there is a daily high tide, a biweekly high, and a perigean high, so in the air there is a daily "high tide" of fog, a weekly high, and a seasonal high. As in the water, the highest of all the fog tides occurs when the three cycles coincide. In the case of the fog, the maximum comes usually just before dawn on an August morning at the end of a weekly cycle.

At such times the top of the fog presses upward against the inversion about 2000 feet. Very rarely it may even overtop Tamalpais at 2600 feet. It pours through Carquinez in masses similar to the advance guard which probed into the Golden Gate, except that the Carquinez invasion is more likely to be several hundred feet above the water because of the normal lifting of the fog as it moves inland.

When the inversion, retreating upward, lifts above the

lower gaps in the Berkeley Hills, the fog creeps through Wildcat Canyon at Tilden Park and spills over into Orinda; it steals over Shepherd Canyon into Moraga; it pours through Niles Canyon into the Livermore Valley. Northward it penetrates the lower Napa and Sonoma valleys, worrying grape growers, who count on sunshine. To the south it rolls over the peninsula hills from the ocean in spectacular cascading fog falls, descends to the oak-studded hills behind Stanford, dampens evening pool-side barbecue parties in the gardens of foothill homes from Los Altos to Saratoga to Los Gatos. It spills through gaps and saddles around Mount Umunhum, Loma Prieta, and Mount Madonna and drifts among the orchards of the Santa Clara Valley. Around Gilroy it may even join another arm of fog coming north from Monterey Bay. To the east it drives up the river channel to the delta and into the heart of the hot Central Valley itself, reaching at times as far as Stockton and Sacramento.

The forces of the sea have penetrated into the inner citadel of the enemy. Their victory, however, is short-lived. They are badly overextended. The fog, attacking under cover of night, has pushed its advance columns to a point nearly one hundred miles inland from the cold ocean currents which gave it birth. It has battled its way upward against the inversion perhaps half a mile into the sky. And, most important, it has cooled much of the Central Valley; in the wake of the sea air and fog, summer temperatures at Stockton and Sacramento may drop from above a hundred into the low eighties. Gone is the intense heat which sucked the cool ocean air through the Gate to replace the rising warm air of the valley. One morning the fog, which may have blanketed the bay and its shores all day for several days, has suddenly vanished. From Napa to San Jose, from the Golden Gate to the delta the air is clear and the waters of the bay once more are bright in the sun.

Even though the fog is gone, the air over the bay is not yet as sharply clear as it will become in the cold days of winter. For a sea breeze, however diminished, still blows through the Gate, bringing minute particles of salt, now invisible except as a faint haze extending upward several hundred or a thousand feet over the bay.

On rare occasions, possibly once or twice a season, the bay experiences a touch of what in much of the rest of the country would be known as normal summer temperatures; even at the Golden Gate the mercury may reach the high eighties. San Franciscans mop their brows, and newspapers break out their "heat wave" headlines, explaining that the city's "natural air-conditioning system" has broken down temporarily.

What occurs at such times is that the ocean's aerial forces have been defeated by an overwhelming counterattack from the air masses of the land. Hot dry air from the valley, reinforced by much larger air movements from the plateaus of inner Oregon, Idaho, and Nevada, move down to the bay and force the cool marine air with its fog out through the Gate and far to sea. Then the bay has a few days of what its summers would be like without the fog canopy—hot, dry, and clear. Beaches are jammed; the lawns of parks can scarcely be seen for the sun-bathers; and office workers proudly show up on the job Monday morning with pink faces and sore backs.

But inevitably the counter-counterattack comes from the ocean, the dry inland air is driven back, the foghorns are heard in the Gate, and once again the city is wrapped in a cool white mantle of privacy.

Smog and Mirages   By September the sun has already moved far south; the air over the continent and the ground beneath it begin to cool off. From Bangor to San Diego the nights are longer and cooler. Across the Great Plains people on farms and in towns wake up in the morning, see the dew on the grass, and know that summer is over. In the high country of Colorado and Utah and Nevada the first frost is already on the pumpkin and the pavement.

But the North Pacific, which during the summer absorbs the sun's heat far more slowly than does the land, is only now reaching its temperature high for the year. As the land cools, the ocean is still growing warmer, and there no longer is much difference in temperature. The ocean winds, which during the spring and summer were rushing landward to replace the rising warm air over the continent, die down in early fall to mild breezes. The bay surface, choppy all summer in the west winds, now often lies still as a pond. Sailboats which leaned sharply in the breeze now find themselves frequently becalmed, sometimes in the middle of a race.

The cold upwelling from the ocean bottom diminishes, and swimmers are grateful. The cycles of fog grow shorter and the intervals of sun longer. When fog does move in through the Gate, it moves more slowly, creeps low over the water, burns off earlier in the day. Without the stiff ocean breezes and the fog canopy San Francisco temperatures rise from the fifties into the sixties and seventies; September and October are the two warmest months of the year.

As the breeze diminishes in strength, the warm inversion layer, no longer lifted high by the intrusions of sea air, falls lower. Climb Tamalpais now, and you will walk from cool to warm air a few hundred feet from the base of the mountain. You can see the inversion pressing down low over the bay. Often 780-foot Mount Ida on Angel Island stands clear above the haze-covered water.

The sea air hangs low over the bay as it did in early spring before the winds began. Smoke particles from the chimneys along the bay's shores, no longer whipped away by the winds, cling to the droplets of moisture in the bay air, increasing the haze.

Thus begins the season of smog. Held in by the mountains which rim the bay and by the inversion acting as a lid, the vapors collect steadily. Smoke rises slowly, flattens out against the bottom of the inversion. A slight movement of air from the ocean in the afternoon will drift the smog eastward and pile it up against the Berkeley Hills.

Unlike the Los Angeles area, where the smog is trapped by eastern mountains several thousand feet high with no low-level passes, the bay is bounded on the east by hills seldom higher than fifteen hundred feet and penetrated at the north end by the sea-level pass at Carquinez. Ocean air entering the Golden Gate not only tends to circulate through Carquinez, but ultimately raises the inversion above the level of the eastern hills, allowing the smog to escape.

As a result, the bay's smog is never as thick as the worst afflicting Los Angeles and seldom lasts more than three or four days. Nevertheless, by 1956 it had become sufficiently obnoxious to result in the formation of the Bay Area Air Pollution Control District, which in its first action ordered the elimination of burning in city dumps along the bay's shores.

The low autumnal inversion may result in other atmospheric changes, some of them freakish. As the breeze through the Gate alternately rises and falls, thin layers of ocean air come in beneath the hazier bay air and lift the haze a few feet off the water. Sometimes the air masses are stacked up several deep, hazy layers sandwiched between relatively clear layers, all within the few hundred feet below the inversion and clearly outlined against the surrounding hills.

Occasionally the bottom of the inversion layer may act as a mirror, reflecting ships and shores above the surface in startling mirages. Boatmen off Sausalito sometimes observe the buildings of downtown Oakland planted firmly in midbay in front of the Bay Bridge. Ships at a distance may be seen double, an inverted image directly over the real one.

And on occasion San Francisco newspaper offices have received calls from beach observers who insisted that the Farallones were hanging upside down in the sky.

The Coming of the Storms   Sometimes in late September or October masses of moist air move north from subtropical Pacific areas off Mexico, bringing to the bay occasional high clouds, possibly showers, and, very rarely, thunderstorms. But usually even November is still calm and warm, with temperatures higher than in April. By this time, however, things are brewing far out over the North Pacific.

The first sign of major change comes when the city's flags, which had been hanging listlessly or waving gently toward the east, begin to stretch out northward. High, feathery cirrus clouds spread a thin veil across the sky, dimming the sun. The red storm flags fly from the mast of the Telephone Building downtown and from the Marine Exchange lookout station on Meiggs Wharf. The wind increases steadily, scuffing up whitecaps on the lead-colored bay. Small boats pitch and throw spray back from their bows.

From off the deeps of the North Pacific, anywhere from the Hawaiian Islands to the Aleutians or the Gulf of Alaska, a low-pressure area of warm air is moving toward the California coast. Around it the winds are circling counterclockwise, blowing over the bay from the south. As the air masses of different temperatures meet, they give birth to clouds and to rain.

The rain comes to the bay slowly, out of a dark gray sky. At first scarcely more than a fine mist, it envelops the hills, moves down to the shores, dampening docks and beaches, stippling the gray surface of the water.

The bay area's diverse hill, valley, and water topography, which gives it such a wide spread of summer temperatures, gives it a great variation of rainfall as well. The rain, coming with the wind from the south, falls most heavily on the southern slopes of the bay's hills. The higher the hills, the more the air is forced upward, the more the clouds cool, the heavier the rain.

Near the tops of the peninsula's Santa Cruz Mountains in the Boulder Creek area, sixty miles south of San Francisco, where the south winds are trapped in the valley of the San Lorenzo River and forced to rise, the rainfall in a season often reaches sixty inches. On the leeward side of the same mountains, the Santa Clara Valley, only twenty miles away, gets only one fourth as much rain.

Storm clouds running into 2600-foot Mount Tamalpais spill great quantities of their burden on its slopes. Kentfield, just beneath the mountain, gets normally more than twice San Francisco's annual twenty-one inches and holds the all-time bay area rainfall record for a single season—eighty-eight inches in the winter of 1889–90.

Occasionally in midwinter the heights around the bay will be whitened by a light snowfall, from a mere dusting on Twin Peaks to several inches on Tamalpais. Snow in downtown San Francisco is very rare, but on a cold February day in 1887, residents were astonished when nearly four inches coated the streets and roofs, setting a record which still stands.

Tule Fog   Storms over the bay can break up in several ways. They may dwindle in a series of windy gusts and separate showers—slanting streamers of rain hung like somber tapestries from dark masses of cloud in a brightening sky. Or they may end suddenly; one morning, after many days of clouded darkness during which you cannot see the far shore, you wake up and the rain is gone. Cold air masses moving in from the ocean behind the storm have swept away all haze;

the air is intensely clear; and for fifty miles the great sheet of blue water sparkles in the sun.

After the rains are gone and the wind dies, when the ground is moist and the air is cold, clear, and still, it is time for another of the bay's weather moods of rare beauty—the winter fog.

Open to the frosty stars, with no cloud cover to hold the heat in, the earth and the air cool quickly. The coldest air sinks to the lowest areas, and as the air grows even colder during the night, its moisture condenses into vapor, hugging the cold ground. The rising sun next morning shines down on low spots covered with diaphanous white mists. As the sun heats the air slightly, causing it to move, the fog slowly drifts in masses or long serpentine forms through the low canyons and valleys and across the bay surface.

As the coldest parts of the bay in winter are those farthest from the moderating influence of the ocean, the winter fog begins to form first in the tule marshes of the delta and Suisun Bay and along the lower river channels. Hence its popular name—tule fog.

Sometimes it spreads from the Suisun-delta region down through Concord and Walnut Creek and Lafayette, east of the Berkeley Hills. There it may pile up in drifts several hundred feet deep against the hills until it pours through the gaps near Roundtop and Canyon and Niles into Berkeley and Oakland and down to the bay. Occasionally, if the weather is unusually cold, tule fog forms over the main part of the bay itself, fills the basin around it, and spills out through the Golden Gate into the ocean, reversing the summertime fog. It was just such a wall of tule fog into which the ill-fated *Rio de Janeiro* sailed for the last time on the morning of February 22, 1901.

It is the low-lying tule fog, more often than the higher summer fog, that closes in the entire bay, setting off a magnificent orchestration of foghorns, ships' whistles, bells, and sirens—signals which the experienced ear can translate into an accurate picture of what is transpiring on the hidden bay. Planes may be stacked several layers deep at both Oakland and San Francisco airports, waiting the word to land. Or they may be diverted to the airport at Half Moon Bay, on the ocean side of the peninsula, which is nearly always closed in by summer ocean fogs but is sheltered by the peninsula hills from the bay's own tule fogs. Often these fogs are so low that the hills of San Francisco float like islands in the sunshine amid a sea of drifting vapors, steamy billows from which the sounds of the city and the bay emerge with startling volume.

Eventually the fog burns off over the land and only the water is covered. First the funnels and masts of ships can be seen moving slowly above the fog level. The pilot of a ship may stand on the bridge of his vessel in clear air under a blue sky, unable to see the water below the mists, which dazzlingly reflect the sun. Funnels of tugboats emerge among fog eddies. Then, in patches, the water itself becomes visible. But it will be an hour or more before there is silence on the bay; the horns continue to moan as the remaining wraiths of the departed fog blanket drift aimlessly across the water, swirling in the wakes of boats, then dissolving into sunshine.

Out of the North   Cold spells on the bay are rare. San Francisco is kept warm in winter, as it is kept cool in summer, by the even-temperatured waters around it. But the popular notion that the "Japanese Current" flows down the California coast—and is responsible for the warm winters—is a myth. The only warm current from Japan reaching the eastern Pacific never gets closer than five hundred miles from the coast.

What does flow down the coast is the California Current, a

cold streak of water from the Aleutians. But warm and cold are relative terms; the winter water temperature in the Golden Gate stays near fifty, cold compared to the sixty-degree Japanese waters, but still warm enough to prevent bay area land temperatures from dropping very far. San Francisco's average temperature in January, the coldest month, is almost exactly the temperature of the water entering the bay on the flood tide.

Thus the bay acts as a natural thermostat; just as the ocean moderates the climate of the continent, so the entire bay cools the summers and warms the winters of the communities on its shores.

Sometimes, however, the movements of the weather take place on such a vast scale that the normal local influences are overwhelmed by far larger outside forces. It is as if a window in a thermostat-controlled room were broken, allowing a sudden flow of air from the outside, hot in summer, cold in winter.

Just as occasional hot spells in summer result from the in-rush of masses of dry continental air from inland valleys and desert areas, so a cold snap will result from similar causes. An imbalance in the normal front of polar and equatorial air over the continent will send icy winds across the snow-covered high plains of Oregon, Idaho, and Nevada, whistling down the Sacramento Valley and through the passes and canyons of the Coast Range, roaring out across the bay from the northeast, whipping it into a froth of whitecaps.

Again the storm warnings go up; this time the Telephone Building mast flies two flags—besides the red pennant, warning small craft, is a square red flag, storm signal for ships as well. Fishermen's fingers grow numb in the icy spray. Towboat pilots curse as the wind swings their barges out of control. Pilots of big freighters and liners try to avoid docking on the north sides of piers where the ships may batter the wharves as they wallow in the wind. In the streets of the bay's cities hats go flying and pedestrians turn up coat collars and huddle in doorways against the cold blasts.

The northers may come at almost any time of year but are most probable in early spring, when the air over the continent is most turbulent. They may blow for two or three days and die out in fits and gusts. Once more the air becomes calm, and the bay is placid before noon, ruffled in later afternoon by gentle ocean breezes.

Then early one morning you may hear, as you rouse to wakefulness, the bass chorus of the great horns. The earth has completed another cycle around the sun; the coastal waters are beginning to well up from the bottom; and a long white arm of fog is once more moving silently through the Golden Gate and over the face of the bay.

NIGHT

Just after sundown the bay is a pool of light in the darkening evening. It seems to have absorbed the sun's radiation during the day and to have stored it up for this time when the sky's light is dying. Against the dark rim of the far hills the silver-gray surface gives the illusion of being curved, like the face of a giant lens.

In this brief moment, when the buildings along the shores have been almost absorbed into the darkness, there comes a quick impression that the shoreline cities have vanished and the scene appears as it did before the coming of man; the only realities are the darkly glowing bay, the black hills, and the sky.

Then, almost imperceptibly, the lights along the far shores begin to glitter in the still clear air—the diamond constellation of Sausalito on its hillside, the scattered points of light across Belvedere and Tiburon, the dense nebulae of Richmond, Berkeley, and Oakland along the eastern foothills.

Momentarily the bay holds the last light of day, then disappears into blackness. Only the lamps on the bridges, swinging like strings of amber jewels over the gulf, are reflected in shimmering paths across the dark water. Elsewhere, under a clear, moonless sky, the bay is an immense void, a place of absolute dark, like a cavern of infinite depth.

High on the rim of the great bowl of hills around the bay the aircraft beacons flash their signal in rapid rhythm, taken up by the red warning lights on the towers of the bridges and by the lighthouses along the shore. From the mountains to the bridges to the bay the signal is passed to the sea; and the circling sweep of the Alcatraz light is answered by quick flashes from Point Bonita, from the lightship beyond the bar, and from the great beacon on the Farallones.

13

The Bridges

THE BRIDGE THAT COULDN'T BE BUILT

The last car to cross the Golden Gate Bridge on the historic afternoon of December 1, 1951, was driven by a young woman named Nancy Kent. The twilight sky was clouded, and a strong wind was blowing as she and a girl friend drove up the mile-long approach ramp and paused at the tollgate; they noticed nothing unusual, however, until they were well out on the bridge itself.

As they passed the south tower, strong gusts of wind pushed the car toward the right, and the sound of the wind in the cables and girders grew steadily to a monstrous howl which drowned out conversation. Miss Kent felt the steering wheel tug first one way then the other. The car began to lurch and pitch strangely. She looked off to the right beyond the deck rail and saw the lights of Fort Baker on the Marin shore whirl crazily like spiraling comets. The bridge deck itself was rolling before the wind like a ship in a high sea.

The two exchanged glances. Then, peering forward and to the rear, they became aware of a terrifying fact: there were no other cars in sight. They were alone on the heaving deck.

Both passengers had crossed the bridge hundreds of times without being aware of any sensation different from that of driving on a road built on solid ground. Now they became acutely conscious of a fact that few of the bridge's commuters ever consider; the roadway is not solid at all but suspended in mid-air on wires and cables, the height of a twenty-story building above the roaring waters of the ocean. Uneasily they recalled the collapse of the suspension bridge at Tacoma, Washington, ripped loose by a high wind a few years before. The thought struck them with sudden impact: If the bridge gave way, there would be a dizzy, spinning fall through space . . .

Miss Kent struggled with the wheel on the writhing roadway for what seemed an interminable time. At last the north tower loomed ahead in the dark sky. As they approached it, the deck motion diminished. Still trembling, they drove off the bridge onto the Marin shore. Across the road was a long line of parked cars, facing the bridge, flagged down by highway patrolmen. For the first time in its fourteen years the bridge had been closed for safety reasons.

For a short time the deserted deck continued to sway and twist before the gale. Then the wind slackened gradually, and the bridge calmed down. Two hours and fifty minutes after it had been closed to traffic, it was reopened. Inspections had disclosed minor damages but no injury to the main structure. The builders of the bridge had built well.

The big storm of 1951 pointed up the most remarkable aspect of this bridge and the fact that made it the supreme achievement in bridge engineering to that time—not merely that it was the longest and highest single span ever constructed but that it was built to defy the full fury of the ocean. Unlike any other large bridge ever built, it is a bridge over the sea. Moreover it spans a part of the sea subject to some of the most violent weather in the world. The pier of one of its twin towers rests deep on the ocean floor itself, and its deck swings high above the tides—in the direct path of storms generated across thousands of miles of the Pacific and hitting the continent with a momentum and impact able to jar the solid rock of the coastal cliffs.

In its first stages the building of the Golden Gate Bridge was a battle of men against the sea.

The Builder   From the days of the Spanish explorers, to whom the bay was simply a barrier to further land travel up the coast, men had dreamed of bridging the Golden Gate. But for a century and a half no one had any idea as to how it could be done. No such strait had ever been spanned. The building of the bridge had to wait for history to catch up with it: It had to wait for the bay shores to be populated sufficiently for the potential traffic to justify a bridge; it had to wait for advances in the science of construction to make a structure of this magnitude even theoretically possible; and it had to wait for a man—the man with the imagination, the skill, the boldness, and the persistence to organize the job and fight the battle to its completion.

Joseph Baermann Strauss, like many men who built large, was small in stature, barely over five feet tall. There is a story that as an undergraduate at the University of Cincinnati he went out for football, became a target of ridicule for his diminutive size, and was so mauled by the behemoths on the squad that he ended up in the hospital. There he convalesced with dreams of glory, developing an obsession with size; he would become an engineer and build the biggest bridge in the world.

The story could well be true; the subject of Strauss's graduate thesis in engineering was a bridge joining North America and Asia across the Bering Strait. By the time of World War I, though still in his mid-forties, he was a world-renowned bridgebuilder. He had constructed scores of bridges in many countries, including one for the Czar across the Neva in Russia and the center span of the Arlington Memorial Bridge in Washington, D.C.

Strauss was an inventor and an innovator. Every new bridge site was a challenge to which he responded with new ideas, some of which revolutionized aspects of bridgebuilding. But the supreme challenge was yet to come.

One day in 1917 during a vacation tour from his home in Chicago, Strauss stood on the hill behind Fort Point overlooking the narrows of the Golden Gate. In front of him the ridge dropped steeply away to the old red brick fort which had once guarded the bay's entrance. Across a mile of blue-green water, the hills of Marin rose in sharp red escarpments hundreds of feet high. Here, where the ocean had breached the coastal mountains, was one of the world's most dramatic meetings of land and water. Here was the strait which had always been considered unbridgeable. Here, Strauss knew instinctively, he would build his greatest bridge.

A year later he presented San Francisco with the first preliminary design for a bridge across the Golden Gate. The plans had been drawn up by Strauss the engineer. But equally important was the element supplied by Strauss the visionary. For engineering was only part of the problem; people had to be convinced that such a bridge could and should be built. From the moment he had stood on the hill overlooking the Gate, Strauss was a dedicated man, seized by a mighty purpose. For him the Golden Gate Bridge was not a problem in engineering; it was a crusade.

His enthusiasm was contagious, and his zeal fired the imaginations of men of power and influence in the bay area. But he also incurred powerful opposition. For more than a decade the engineer and his supporters fought a series of complex political and legal battles for the right to build the bridge. In the opposition were ferryboat operators afraid of being put out of business, military leaders and shippers who feared the bridge would bottle up the harbor, businessmen who believed that any attempt to bridge the Gate would be a financial and engineering fiasco. Thirteen engineers, including the city engineer of San Francisco, signed statements opposing the project; and a San Francisco banker called it "an economic crime."

But Strauss and his backers succeeded in convincing the highest authority, the voters. In 1930 the people of the six coastal counties in the Golden Gate Bridge District approved bonds for the bridge by a three-to-one majority.

Still the bonds had to be sold. It was at the bottom of the Depression. Most bond houses politely declined to buy; the bridge was too speculative. Marin County was still sparsely settled, and there was no assurance that the bridge would ever carry enough traffic to pay for itself.

Strauss, undismayed, took his problem to the founder of the Bank of America, the financial giant of the West, Amadeo Peter Giannini. In the granite-jawed financier Strauss found the imagination and daring he was looking for. Genius communicated with genius.

"San Francisco needs that bridge," Giannini was quoted as saying. "We'll take the bonds."

The Fight against the Sea   Having defeated the human

opposition, Strauss next confronted even more formidable opponents—the elements.

Long ago he had made his plans for the bridge's foundations. The north pier could be built on the rocks at the water's edge, but the south pier would have to be constructed underwater in the mighty currents of the Gate, a task for which there was no precedent in engineering history.

Fortunately there was a submarine shelf of rock extending out from the southern shore—the Fort Point shoal, where the *Rio de Janeiro* had been wrecked in 1901. The first job was to build a working trestle 1100 feet long to get men and equipment to the point over the shoal where the south tower was to be planted, sixty-five feet below the surface.

In the struggle between men and the sea, several times during the first year—1933—it looked as if the sea would win. One foggy August day, after eight months of preliminary work, an inbound freighter loomed out of the murk, plowed through the trestle, and sent one hundred feet of it to the bottom. In November, heavy seas battered the rebuilt trestle, knocked off the working equipment at the end, and sank three house-sized concrete blocks that were to have been used in the foundation. Six weeks later an even greater storm lashed the coast; waves twenty feet high charged in from the Pacific and ripped out three quarters of the entire trestle. Stubbornly Strauss began all over again; this time he built a king-sized trestle that succeeded in withstanding the worst that the Pacific could do.

Meanwhile construction was threatened by the Battle of the Geologists. Strauss's chief consultant on the bridge's rock foundation was white-bearded, seventy-two-year-old Dr. Andrew C. Lawson of the University of California, renowned authority on local geology. His approval of the site for the south pier was challenged by white-bearded, seventy-six-year-old Dr. Bailey Willis, equally renowned geologist at rival Stanford University.

Willis was well known to newspaper readers for what seemed uncanny accuracy in predicting earthquakes. Ten years earlier he had made a speech in Santa Barbara warning residents of the danger of quake action along nearby faults. Shortly afterward, the city was jolted by a disastrous temblor. His denials that he had known when the quake was coming failed to dim his fame in the public prints, where he became known as "Earthquake" Willis.

Now a decades-long rivalry between the two venerable geologists flared anew when Willis issued a widely publicized blast against Lawson and the bridgebuilders. The rock on which the south tower was to be built, he said, was weak serpentine "pudding stone," subject to landslides and "unstable to a degree likely to endanger the structure."

Lawson's reply resounded across the bay from Berkeley to Stanford. "Buncombe!" he snorted. The Stanford geologist, he declared, had made a business of frightening the public with his scarehead talk about earthquakes and now, in trying to alarm people about the bridge, was simply up to his old tricks. Thorough investigation, Lawson asserted, had proved the basic rock perfectly sound.

Lawson was solidly backed up by Strauss. But the Stanford scientist's report nevertheless had its effect. The bridge's opponents gloated; and in Washington PWA officials read Willis's charges and frowned on the possibility of helping finance construction.

Willis had indicated that the "danger" to the bridge could be overcome by deepening the foundation. Actually, before his charges were made public, Strauss had planned to deepen the foundation, and it was finally laid at one hundred feet below the surface, thirty-five feet deep into the bedrock.

Willis later noted with satisfaction that the base had been

deepened. Whether it was deep enough, he added cryptically, only time would tell.

The South Pier   Despite the attacks of men and the ocean the work went on.

"The construction of the south pier," Strauss said later, "was without question the most difficult engineering feat men have ever attempted."

To build a foundation for the bridge on an uneven, sloping rock floor was difficult enough; to do so in the furious currents of the Gate—even Strauss admitted—was impossible. Divers and equipment would be swept away on every tide. The only solution was to secure some sort of protection. Strauss conceived the idea of completely enclosing the site with a concrete breakwater, or fender, in order to have quiet water in which to work.

The currents were so swift that divers could work for only an hour four times a day between tides. In these intervals of slack water they planted dynamite to blast deep into the serpentine bedrock, then lowered steel shells into which the concrete for the fender was poured. The fender walls were about thirty feet thick and five stories high. Just before the structure was finished, an opening was left in one side in order that a huge floating steel caisson could be towed in. Then the fender would be permanently closed. In the still water inside the caisson would be sunk by filling it with concrete, providing a foundation for the pier.

The ticklish job of towing the big steel box into place inside the fender was accomplished on the scheduled day without a hitch. But before the fender could be closed, the ocean again took charge. Strauss was awakened in the middle of the night by an excited superintendent with an alarming story: Great swells were rolling in from the Pacific, pouring through the hole in the fender and tossing the caisson against the surrounding concrete with a thunderous impact that could be heard halfway across the city. The caisson, lifted on the waves, was the irresistible force; the fender was the immovable object.

Strauss did not wait to see which would win out. Fearing one or both would be destroyed, he made a drastic decision: The caisson would have to be sacrificed. It was towed out of the enclosure and sunk in deep water.

One more battle had been won by the ocean, and the bridge's opponents had another inning. But Strauss was not easily baffled. Defeated in one approach, he switched his entire strategy for building the south pier. Instead of using a caisson he closed up the fender, laid down an underwater concrete floor forty feet thick, then pumped the water out, leaving a dry area inside the size of a football field. Thus the south pier was built "in the dry," while the tides swirled around the concrete walls. The fender, filled again with water to maintain even pressure, was left permanently in place, protecting the pier from storms and ships.

The Human Cost　　With the completion of the south pier the greatest fight against the elements had been won. But even more spectacular was the spinning of the two giant cables from which the deck was to be suspended. On each side of the channel two big shuttles moved back and forth from anchorage to midspan; each carried a total of 27,252 strands of pencil-thick wire—enough to circle the earth three times—binding them into a cable 36½ inches in diameter and 7650 feet long.

As a veteran bridgebuilder, Strauss was highly conscious of the axiom: "The bridge demands its life." Traditionally accidents are responsible for one death per million dollars of bridge. Considering the extremely hazardous conditions under which the $33,000,000 Golden Gate Bridge was built, the death rate might easily have been twice normal. But Strauss was convinced he could beat the odds.

Workmen were given special diets to counteract dizziness and special goggles to prevent sun blindness when working high above the white fogs which often roll in just over the water. They drank special sauerkraut juice "chasers" to counteract a morning hangover. And any employee with a tendency to show off by stunting on the bridge was fired on the spot.

The builder realized that despite all these precautions the factor of human error could not be eliminated; almost inevitably there would be occasions when men would lose their footing and plunge toward the water hundreds of feet below —to almost certain death on impact. So he developed his greatest safety innovation: a giant net, strung beneath the entire bridge from shore to shore. Those who quarreled with his judgment in spending $80,000 for the strange contraption were silenced when over a period of months nineteen men tumbled from their lofty perches and bounced harmlessly in the net. They formed the exclusive "Halfway to Hell" club.

As a result of Strauss's safety precautions, in the first four years of construction there was not a single life lost. Then early in 1937 the perfect record was broken when a derrick toppled over and killed one man. Shortly afterward, within three months of the bridge's completion, a dozen workmen were standing on a temporary wooden platform beneath the deck, removing boards from the concrete roadway, when a corner bracket of the platform snapped. The added weight on the other brackets was too great; the entire platform ripped loose, plunging toward the bay with its human cargo.

The net had not been designed for the several thousand pounds of men and wood and steel that came hurtling down from above. It sagged, stretched, and tore with a resounding rip. Platform, men, and half the net plummeted into the outgoing tide two hundred feet below. Nine of the bodies were swept out to sea. Two men who miraculously escaped death were fished out of the water, badly injured. And one workman was discovered dangling desperately from the underside of the deck, scared but unhurt, his pipe still clenched firmly in his teeth.

Triumph   Bay area residents watched with awe and pride as the structure grew to its full size. Strauss's original plan for a steel cantilever bridge with a suspension span in the middle had been changed to a single suspension span. The suspended deck, including the 4200-foot center span and the two side spans, was 90 feet wide and 6450 feet long. The approach structures added another half mile. (Part of the southern approach was a steel arch especially designed to overleap the historic old fort.)

The tops of the stepped-back steel towers were a dizzy 750 feet above the water—nearly twice as high as San Francisco's tallest buildings. Their solid appearance was deceptive; they consisted of hollow steel cells. Inside the eastern column of each of the towers was an elevator for workmen. Watchmen and inspectors were given a twenty-six-page manual to chart their way around inside the labyrinth. The manual was published after two workmen got lost in the north tower and had to spend the night inside before groping their way back to daylight the next morning.

Strauss designed his bridge with a safety factor of 2.6. This meant that the deck would support the weight of cars and trucks jammed bumper to bumper in all six lanes, plus enough pedestrians on the sidewalks to occupy every available inch of standing room—even if a hurricane wind were to blow at the same time.

In May 1937, just twenty years after Strauss first stood on the hill above Fort Point and dreamed of bridging the Golden Gate, his masterpiece was completed. San Francisco observed the event with all-out celebrations. After several days of parades, parties, and ceremonies, thousands of people jammed Crissy Field in the Presidio near the base of the bridge to watch a spectacular historical pageant, climaxed as John Charles Thomas and the massed choirs sang "Hymn to the Rainbow."

The bridge's first day was reserved for pedestrians, and more than two hundred thousand made the hike. The first man across had to be content with a small share of the glory. Dozens of less speedy pedestrians contrived to be first in one way or another. Among those claiming titles were the first person to cross on stilts; the first twins; the first mother pushing a baby carriage; the first person to cross walking backward; the first dog; the first musician to cross tooting a tuba all the way; and the first two people to make the trip carrying twenty-five pounds of anthracite coal from their home town in Pennsylvania.

There were several faintings and falls. Police hurried to help one woman who was staggering along with her mouth open and her tongue protruding, but they were brushed aside impatiently; she was aspiring to be the first person to cross with her tongue out.

It is said that after a bridge is finished the engineers begin another battle to keep it from falling down. On the Golden Gate Bridge that battle costs about $2200 a day. Twenty-five painters are constantly engaged in the fight against rust, climbing over and under the bridge and applying two tons of paint a week to its towers, girders, cables, and steel ropes. The paint—"international orange"—is not only the most resistant to sun, wind, fog, rain, and salt spray, it also is the color most readily visible in fog. There were early plans to paint the bridge with a rainbow effect—darker at the ends, shading lighter toward the middle—and nearly every day someone suggests that it be painted gold. Fortunately both proposals have been rejected.

The Bending Bridge   Besides the tides and sea storms with which Strauss had to contend in the early stages his greatest problems in designing and constructing the bridge were heat and moving air. As Aesop once advised, the sun is stronger than the wind. Strauss said that a single hour of bright sun would have greater effect on the bridge than a hurricane.

To cope with both elements, the bridge was designed for maximum flexibility, enabling it to roll with the punches. For the layman who conceives of steel as rigid, the bridge's flexibility is a source of wonder. Normally the deck arches upward slightly. In driving across the central span of the bridge a motorist climbs about twenty feet to the center before starting downhill again. In cold weather the cables contract, pulling the arch even higher.

On hot days the cables lengthen, and the deck center drops toward the water. The weight of heavy traffic also can flatten out the arch to some degree. The center of the deck can rise and fall from all causes a total of about sixteen feet. The resulting differences in the length of the deck are taken up in the expansion joints, the largest of which consist of five hundred interlocking steel fingers across the roadway at each tower.

Thus temperatures and traffic as well as tides determine how much clearance the bridge allows for ships. On a cold night at low tide with no traffic the center clearance would be as much as 242 feet. On a hot day with heavy traffic at high tide it could diminish to 220 feet. During World War II, when the *Queen Elizabeth* entered the bay, she had to come in at high tide in order to have sufficient depth to maneuver into the dock; with the reduced clearance she scraped beneath the center of the bridge with a bare two feet to spare.

The towers themselves are also flexible. Their position is controlled by the cables, which are attached to the tower tops. At normal temperatures, when there is no traffic on the deck, the towers were designed to lean a few inches away from each other. A heavy traffic load pulling on the cables, or hot weather causing them to lengthen, will result in the tower tops moving closer together.

The winds, roaring in from the Pacific and funneling through the narrows of the Gate, would be more dangerous to a completely rigid structure than to a flexible one. Strauss designed his bridge to withstand hurricane winds by swaying a maximum of 27.7 feet out of line at the center. Even in the big blow which closed the bridge in 1951, the sideward sway was only a fraction of the maximum. The motion that caused the trouble was not the side sway but an unanticipated twist. The wind, instead of coming from the west as usual, blew in from the southwest and set up a series of oscillations in the deck. At one point on the span the east rail of the deck would be raised as much as eleven feet higher than the west rail; at another point half a mile distant the deck would be simultaneously twisted in the opposite direction. This was the same kind of motion, set up by a forty-two-mile wind, that had doomed the Tacoma suspension bridge in 1940, but the Golden Gate Bridge, more sturdily constructed, was able to sustain even this violent distortion in a sixty-nine-mile blow without substantial damage. As a result of a subsequent survey by Clifford E. Paine, Strauss's chief assistant during construction and now Consulting Engineer to the Bridge District, the bridge was "stiffened" with $3,500,000 worth of new lateral girders twenty-five feet beneath the deck to prevent such oscillations in the future.

Strauss himself was not present to give advice after the 1951 storm. Exactly a year after the bridge's opening the chief engineer, fatigued from the years of intense strain and constant responsibility, died of a heart attack at the age of sixty-eight.

At the lookout point just below the bridge's toll plaza stands a bronze statue of the builder of the bridge. It is the figure of a small, delicately featured man who looks more like a poet or an artist than an engineer. And Strauss in fact was a poet; several of his verses have been published in anthologies. But pre-eminently he was a poet in steel. His greatest poem is the long graceful span soaring above the swift waters of the strait.

THE BIGGEST BRIDGE IN THE WORLD

It is possibly the most remarkable coincidence in the history of engineering that the bay's two great bridges were planned and built simultaneously. Although both had been dreamed of for many generations, they were constructed by different organizations, are operated under different management, and are unconnected in any way, largely because of the different nature of each project.

The Golden Gate Bridge was a speculation, both in engineering and economics. Its construction, by a local district with no government aid, took place when it did largely because of the promotional genius of Joseph B. Strauss.

The San Francisco-Oakland Bay Bridge, on the other hand, was an official project almost from the start. Nearly everyone agreed that such a bridge was necessary. The great stream of ferry commuters to the East Bay was solid assurance that a San Francisco-Oakland bridge would be able to pay for itself out of tolls. It was planned and constructed by the state of California with a loan from the federal government.

Like the Golden Gate Bridge, however, there was initial doubt as to whether it could be built. This was the widest navigable stretch of water men had ever contemplated bridging, nearly three times as wide as the Firth of Forth in Scotland, crossed by the then-longest high-level bridge in the world. A bridge to Oakland would be midway between two major earthquake faults and would have to find a solid foundation on the muddy bay bottom. Government engineers investigating the possibilities in 1924 turned thumbs down on any such proposal.

Luckily the project found a friend in the White House. Herbert Hoover, as an engineer and bay area resident, took a special interest in the idea. With Governor Young of California he appointed the Hoover-Young Commission, which had preliminary surveys made. Later the President speeded War and Navy departments approval, and his Reconstruction Finance Corporation promised financial support.

Some of the most strenuous objections to a bridge had come from San Franciscans who feared that it would mar the scenic beauty of the bay and the city. Their fears proved largely justified when the original designs were submitted, calling for a cantilever-type bridge from San Francisco to Yerba Buena Island and another of the same type from Yerba Buena to Oakland. Heavy masses of steel girders looming above the city and the bay would have been about as aesthetic as New York's Third Avenue El—and twenty times as big.

Fortunately, as the designs evolved, the engineers began to favor the idea of a suspension bridge for the San Francisco half of the crossing. A design similar to the kind planned for the Golden Gate would be not only more beautiful but perhaps even less expensive. But was it feasible?

The Concrete Island   The man who had to find the answer to the big question was the project's chief engineer, Charles Henry Purcell, who as state highway engineer had been secretary of the Hoover-Young Commission. He had learned from the engineers' surveys for the commission that beneath the bay's bottom mud there was a ridge of rock, running from San Francisco's Rincon Hill to Yerba Buena, which could conceivably furnish the necessary solid anchorage for a suspension bridge. But the top of the ridge, unlike the relatively shallow ledge on which the Golden Gate Bridge was to be constructed, was beneath one hundred feet of water and another one hundred feet of mud—deeper than any bridge foundation ever built.

Purcell had another problem—the bay's great width. There were two miles of deep water between the Embarcadero and the island. A suspension bridge two miles long was impossible. But one a mile long was well within reason. Why not reach Yerba Buena with two mile-long spans?

The two bridges would need a surface anchorage between them, halfway to Yerba Buena, to grip their cables. If only there had been another island at that point, Purcell thought, the solution would have been easy. Like Strauss, Purcell had a mind that was not only creative but daring. Why not build an island?

Constructing an ordinary island would have been fairly easy, a simple matter of dumping in enough loose rock, gravel, and sand to rise above the water. But such a fill would not supply the strength necessary to hold the thousands of tons of tension from the cables. The island would have to be not only anchored to the bedrock but as solid as the rock itself.

And it would have to rise more than two hundred feet above the water to support the bridge's deck, in all as high as San Francisco's tallest buildings.

Could such a thing be done? Purcell didn't know. But he knew where to get advice. He went to New York to see Daniel E. Moran, the top expert on deep-water foundations and builder of the piers for New York's George Washington Bridge.

Even Moran lifted his eyebrows at Purcell's question. The island would have to be planted two hundred feet below the surface, nearly twice as deep as the lowest point at which divers could continuously work. But the New Yorker, like the Californian, was capable of rising to a challenge. He went to work on his drawing boards and succeeded in planning an "island" for the middle of the bay. Purcell knew then that the double suspension bridge was possible, at least on paper.

Following Moran's plan, workmen at the Moore drydock in Oakland put together a steel box, or caisson, half the size of a city block, open at the top. Into the box they built fifty-five vertical steel cylinders each fifteen feet in diameter, giving the big box the appearance of a mammoth egg crate. Each of the cylinders was open at the bottom but sealed at the top by a steel dome.

Then the caisson was slid down the ways into the bay and towed to its site halfway between San Francisco and Yerba Buena. Over a period of weeks, concrete from floating mixers was poured into the spaces between the cylinders, sinking the box lower into the water as its sides were built up compensatingly higher. As the bottom of the box sank, the cylinders themselves were lengthened at the top and resealed by the domes.

Thus Moran's island was built from the surface down. When it reached the bottom, sharp lower cutting edges sliced into the muddy bay floor. The cylinders were uncapped, and clamshell-type buckets went down through them and scooped up the mud—6800 pounds of it per gulp. In this way the caisson was rammed one hundred feet down through the layers of mud until it reached the long-sought ridge of bed-rock.

Sharp-pointed steel gads were dropped down through the cylinders to break up the rock, leveling the top of the ridge. Then concrete was poured down through the cylinders, anchoring the structure to the rock. Finally, built up two hundred feet above the water, Moran's island was completed, ready to hold the 40,000-ton tension of the cables in an unbreakable grip.

The monumental island was bigger than the largest of the Pyramids. More concrete had been poured into it than had been used in the Empire State Building. It was one of the wonders of modern engineering.

The Leaning Pier   Chief diver Bill Reed was a key man in the sinking of both the island and the bridge's piers, which were also built from the top down by the caisson method. Reed got $15,000 a year plus a dollar a foot for every dive— and he well deserved it. Although no diver could work continuously at the depths to which the piers were sunk—the pressure there was one hundred pounds per square inch— Reed was able to descend for ten to fifteen minutes at a time for inspection purposes. After each such dive, he would be rushed to a decompression chamber to ease him gradually back to surface air pressures.

In the bay's murky depths there was no light; Reed had to work blind. His fingers were the "eyes" of the engineers. He explored the bay bottom amid anchors, cables, rocks, and unidentifiable debris. On one occasion he found that his lifeline had become inextricably fouled on a cable; he had to cut it loose and be hauled up by his air hose, a highly ticklish procedure.

At one point the caisson for the pier nearest Yerba Buena nearly met disaster. As its bottom was lowered through the mud, it began to emulate the tower of Pisa, tilting precariously out of line. A million dollars' worth of caisson teetered in the balance. Reed descended to the bottom of the leaning concrete, felt his way carefully along the higher edge, and found it hung up on a large boulder. He carefully planted dynamite, which disintegrated the rock, and the caisson swung slowly back into position.

As in the construction of the Golden Gate Bridge, the most difficult part of the job had been done under water. With a few differences the towers were reared, the cables spun, and the decks built in much the same way on both bridges.

The eastern half of the Bay Bridge, between Yerba Buena and Oakland, was a different story. There the architects and engineers had to yield to the geologists—and the economists.

East of Yerba Buena bedrock drops off sharply to depths of several hundred feet. To go that deep through water, sand, and mud to secure an anchorage for a suspension bridge would have required more money than was available. So the engineers decided on the cheaper, cantilever-type construction, capable of being built here because its pressure is exerted straight down; there is no such side pull as would be exerted by cable anchorages for a suspension span.

Purcell's most anxious moments—after the underwater work—were in closing the east span, lifting the 21,000-ton cantilever section from barges into the final 96-foot gap. Bridge officials assembled for the event. Giant cranes hoisted the section 185 feet above the water into position. Then came the hitch.

The mathematicians had figured the fit down to the last fraction of an inch, but they had been unable to predict the weather. At the crucial moment a cold wind came blowing in from the Gate, cooling the north side of the span, and a warm sun beat down from the opposite direction, heating and expanding the south side. The workmen who were to put the last rivets in place found that the span failed to fit by four inches. The riveting had to be postponed for several hours until the weather evened things up.

To connect the two principal sections of the bridge, the world's largest-diameter tunnel was blasted through the center of Yerba Buena—a hole so big that a four-story house could be towed through intact. Its full size is not visible to anyone passing through it, however, since like the bridge itself the tunnel was built with two decks, the upper with six lanes for passenger-car traffic, the lower with three lanes for trucks and busses plus two tracks for electric trains.

A Flood of Cars   On November 12, 1936, after three years and six months of work, the bridge's 6500 builders and several hundred thousand bay area residents celebrated the opening. The bay shores resounded to the cannonading of salutes from fourteen naval ships, and the skies roared with formations of 250 Navy planes. Herbert Hoover made the dedicatory speech; from Washington President Roosevelt pressed a gold key that signaled the opening; and three solid columns of automobiles started from each end of the bridge. High above, a plane wrote in smoke across the sky: "THE BRIDGE IS OPEN."

Newspaper statisticians had a field day. They informed readers that this was the biggest bridge in the world; it was four and a quarter miles long, with another four miles of approaches, and was suspended from cables twenty-eight inches thick. It cost $77,200,000, contained 70,000 miles of pencil-thick wire, 29 miles of main and secondary cables and 22,000,000 rivets. Its towers were 519 feet above the water; its deck offered 216 feet clearance for ships at low tide and was capable of carrying a load of 7000 pounds per foot; and its sodium lamps each gave off the light of thirty-five full moons.

Because of its double deck and greater load capacity the suspension section of the Bay Bridge is far less flexible than the span at the Golden Gate. Although it was designed to sway six feet out of line if necessary, a seventy-five-mile hurricane-force wind was able to budge it only ten inches. Normal breezes, plus traffic vibrations, cause the deck to rise and fall slowly about two inches. But it is so long that temperature changes and variations in the weight of traffic over its 10,000-foot length are theoretically capable of causing it to stretch a total of sixteen feet into the expansion joints.

The most frenetically busy of the bridge's three hundred employees are the hard-working toll collectors, whose calloused palms intercept every cent of the $8,000,000 a year paid out by motorists. They are protected from electric shocks by wire brushes protruding from the roadway to furnish each passing car with a ground wire.

Regularly the collectors are requested to deliver messages to passing drivers. Cross-country motorists headed for San Francisco are often stopped for emergency notification of such news as a death or illness at home, and San Francisco hotels frequently request the collectors to intercept the cars of guests who departed without remembering to take all their baggage.

Some interceptions are more exciting. Whenever San Francisco or East Bay banks are held up, police ask collectors to watch for license numbers of the getaway cars and notify the highway patrol when they pass. On one occasion a steel-nerved collector, notified that a bank robbers' car was approaching his gate, stopped the car ahead of the bandits and chatted casually with the driver while police apprehended the criminals, waiting impatiently to pay their toll.

As an experiment in traffic control, bridge officials allowed a local radio station to originate a program from the dispatcher's office at the toll plaza, beaming it at weary rush-hour drivers on the bridge. Along with music and news, the broadcast supplied up-to-the-minute information on traffic conditions, such as the location of accidents, stalled cars, and other obstructions. The experiment paid off, appreciably reducing bridge accidents.

The calculations of the bridge's engineers and mathematicians, minutely accurate as to the physics of construction, were inadequate to deal with the most baffling of all phenomena—the actions of human beings.

The conservative estimate was that in the bridge's first year, 1937, it would carry 6,000,000 vehicles and that traffic would increase steadily until in 1950 the figure would reach 9,000,000. Amazingly, the traffic reached the 1950 estimate the first year. By 1950 migration to California had reached tidal-wave proportions—a wave partly visible every day on the bridge's deck at rush hour when cars were jammed bumper to bumper, moving at a snail's pace, and sometimes less. Instead of the estimated 9,000,000 vehicles that year, the total reached an astounding 29,000,000. Often the bridge trip across the bay took longer than the former running time of the ferries. By 1956 the count was well over 33,000,000 and still going up rapidly.

Thus within two decades the traffic was already exceeding by one third the structure's calculated optimum capacity. The bridge was a serious bottleneck in the bay area economy. The solution seemed inescapable: more bridges. But the problem of how and where new crossings were to be built was one which riled tempers on both sides of the bay for more than a decade.

THE LESSER SPANS

A Half Century of Bridges   The fame of the two biggest bridges has eclipsed the fact that the bay had been spanned several times previously and that new crossings are still being constructed.

The bay's first bridge was a railroad trestle built in 1906 by the Southern Pacific at the narrows of the shallow southern part of the bay between Dumbarton Point and the Palo Alto area. The first automobiles to cross the bay under their own power chugged jubilantly over the new low-level, three-mile Dumbarton automobile bridge just north of the S.P. trestle, in January of 1927. Although it was constructed as a drawbridge to allow passage for ships to the far end of the bay, the only vessels sailing in that area—aside from an occasional barge—were small boats from yacht harbors at Palo Alto and Alviso. For many years, whenever there was a large northward migration of these craft, such as on the occasions when the California-Stanford Big Game was held in Berkeley, bridge attendants were kept busy hoisting the lift span to allow the passage of each sailboat, then lowering it again to accommodate irate honking motorists bound for the same event. The bottleneck was finally broken when the yacht clubs agreed to convoy their vessels through in a single group.

The first of the bay's high-level bridges was the spectacular four-thousand-foot cantilever structure built in 1927 across the "inner Golden Gate" at Carquinez, with a three-lane deck high enough to allow the passage of ships to Stockton. It was the first bridge in the world specifically designed to withstand earthquakes.

Two years later the bay was spanned again, this time by a low-level drawbridge at the midpoint of the lower bay near

San Mateo. With a total length of twelve miles, seven of them over water, the San Mateo Bridge was the longest highway bridge in the world at the time of its completion. Big Game day held no terrors for its attendants; profiting by the experience of the operators of the Dumbarton Bridge, its builders allowed a thirty-five-foot clearance for the passage of small boats without raising the lift span.

In another respect, however, California-Stanford rivalry was responsible for a memorable episode in the bridge's history. One day in 1930 a group of daring Stanford undergraduates recaptured the historic Stanford Axe at a University of California rally in Berkeley and headed down the east shore in a fast car, pursued by hordes of U.C. students. According to legend, they were able to make their getaway to Palo Alto because the attendant on the San Mateo Bridge, a Stanford man, raised the lift span in time to halt the Berkeley pursuers.

Spanning various arms of the bay are several smaller bridges, such as the Southern Pacific railroad bridge between Martinez and Benicia, the drawbridge at Antioch over the San Joaquin channel, and the new curving concrete span over Richardson Bay just north of Sausalito.

The newest of the bay's seven major crossings, opened in 1956, is the state-constructed Richmond-San Rafael Bridge across the north bay. Replacing the ferry line across the same route, the double-decked, four-mile-long structure can be ranked as one of the two longest high-level bridges in the world. The Bay Bridge, though slightly longer and much greater in total size, is actually two bridges connected by a tunnel. Architecturally the new bridge is less notable; its curious built-in sag in the middle between the two cantilever spans caused some bay area residents to dub it the roller-coaster bridge.

The Southern Crossing   Five additional major bridges to be built by the state are under construction or on the drawing boards. A new crossing at Carquinez, twin to the original span, is due to be finished in 1958. A similar structure is scheduled to cross the strait a few miles to the east between Martinez and Benicia, replacing the bay's last auto ferry. An eventual second bridge is planned for the vicinity of the Golden Gate, probably a double suspension span, resembling the west half of the Bay Bridge, from San Francisco to Tiburon via Angel Island. And a "Southern Crossing" is planned from San Francisco to the east shore, taking some of the load off the overburdened Bay Bridge.

Seldom in the history of the bay area has there been such sound and fury over a civic issue as there was concerning the location of a new bridge from San Francisco to the East Bay. Immediately after World War II it was evident that a new crossing was urgently needed. But where would it be built?

Some planners proposed that a twin of the Bay Bridge be erected parallel and immediately north of it. Others objected strenuously. They argued that a parallel bridge would be highly vulnerable in case of atomic attack, that it would bring more traffic into congested areas, and that the new bridge should be built to the south, between the Hunters Point area and Alameda, in the direction of population growth.

State engineers made detailed studies and in 1948 came up with a recommendation that might have at first seemed to satisfy everyone: Build both bridges. But there was one proviso in the report that put the fight right back where it started. To build both simultaneously would be financially impractical; therefore the parallel bridge should be built first. Among the reasons: "Approximately 82% of the present transbay traffic will be best served by a parallel bridge, and the remaining 18% will be best served by a Southern Crossing.

These percentages will remain substantially unchanged through 1970."

But the Southern Crossing advocates were not convinced. To complicate the situation, they were split among themselves as to whether there should be a trestle-and-tunnel crossing just north of the Hunters Point Naval Shipyard or a cheaper high-level or drawbridge span just south of it at Candlestick Point.

In the midst of the battle architect Frank Lloyd Wright arrived in San Francisco, surveyed the situation, and, with characteristic Olympian disdain for the puny schemes of lesser men, presented his own design for the Southern Crossing—a breath-taking concrete arch, sweeping high above the water and spreading at the center "like a butterfly wing" to make room for lawns, flowers, and an observation park. Despite wide publicity, general enthusiasm, and a public display of a large model of the structure in the San Francisco Museum of Art, no detailed study has been made of its cost or practicability, and as a result it has not been a serious contender.

After a good deal of political pulling and hauling, the legislature authorized a Southern Crossing from Army Street in San Francisco (just north of Hunters Point) to Bay Farm Island, south of Alameda; it would be a trestle bridge except for the main ship channel, where traffic would tunnel under the bay. The bridge would be curved to the south to avoid the Navy's mid-bay seaplane landing zone, and its roundabout approaches would require residents of downtown Oakland and most of Alameda to drive several miles south and east to Bay Farm Island before they could cross going west. One San Francisco engineer suggested that if such a bridge were built, the legislature's next step should be to appropriate money for enough dynamite to blow it up.

Trestle or Butterfly Wing?   Before construction of the

Southern Crossing was begun, an event occurred which threw the entire bridge picture into a new focus. The Bay Area Rapid Transit Commission presented a comprehensive plan that would presumably relieve the transbay traffic situation without any Southern Crossing. The commission proposed a network of rail lines, mostly underground, linking all shores of the bay by electric trains traveling at a top speed of seventy miles per hour. The San Francisco-East Bay line would tunnel beneath the bay, and the San Francisco-Marin line would run on the Golden Gate Bridge or—more probably—on the proposed bridge parallel to it.

There were two big questions to be answered about the rapid-transit plan before any final conclusion could be drawn: Could it be paid for? And would people use it or insist on driving their own cars across the crowded bridges?

Although a rapid-transit plan would presumably make it unnecessary to build a new bridge immediately, the growth of the bay area would seem to make it inevitable that new bridges will be constructed sooner or later. And the planners of future bridges might well ponder some fundamental questions: What is the purpose of a bridge? Should it simply provide the cheapest and quickest way to transport vehicles from one point to another? Or should it also be a work of art, such as Frank Lloyd Wright's "butterfly-wing" bridge?

Fortunately the Golden Gate Bridge and the San Francisco side of the Bay Bridge were able to fulfill both functions. By coincidence the least expensive type of crossing also happened in both cases to be the most beautiful. But what is to happen when the best bridge from the standpoint of appearance is not necessarily the cheapest?

At present architects are severely limited by the requirement that a bridge must pay for itself out of tolls. There is no valid reason, however, why bridges, any more than highways or schools, should be required to pay for themselves out of direct revenues. To be bound by orthodox methods of financing may well be to condemn the bay to mediocrity in its future bridges. This generation of bay area citizens has need of its own Strausses, Purcells, and Gianninis—men of mighty vision. It has need of bridges which are monuments worthy of this bay.

Bridges as Symbols   The great bridges of history have been expressions of the spirit of the civilizations which produced them. Perhaps because a bridge is both a joining together and a means of expanding human freedom, men have long recognized bridges as symbols of human and religious values.

In Roman and medieval times the major bridges were in the custody of priests who tended them with appropriate ceremonies, and often in the Middle Ages a chapel was built directly into the structure itself. Two of Europe's most renowned bridges, "Le Pont d'Avignon" and old London Bridge, became so much a part of the culture as to be enshrined in song and rhyme, and the latter bridge, lined with buildings, was the center of London life for six hundred years. Brooklyn Bridge, the first of the great modern spans, was not only a tremendous engineering achievement on the part of John and Washington Roebling, its builders, but has been recognized in art and poetry as the first large-scale evidence that the Machine Age could create beauty as well as efficiency.

In a different way the two great suspension bridges across San Francisco Bay are symbolic of the people and the times which produced them. Like twentieth-century America at its best, they combine strength with grace; they are mighty without being ponderous; they are powerful without making their power ostentatiously evident.

The bridges derive their fullest significance, however, from their incomparable location on the bay. The Bay Bridge is seen and understood best from a distance, where the entire structure and its setting are in full view. See it from the ferry, crossing from Oakland, in the early evening when the water beneath it still holds the light, the silver steel towers rise high in the afterglow, and the amber lamps of its decks sweep across the sky to the dark hills and inner-lighted skyscrapers of the city. Watch it from San Francisco on a misty day when the water and the sky are a uniform gray, the far shore is invisible, and the bridge seems to be crossing undefined space toward some unknown dimension in the fog.

See it from the north on one of those clear cold days in winter when the cities and mountains of the far circling shore are visible behind it. From here the bridge seems to embrace the entire assemblage of communities around the southern bay for a hundred miles. The lanes of traffic on its deck are vital urban arteries. Yet while uniting the bay's cities it stands above and apart from them in a dimension of its own. From most of downtown San Francisco, to see its deck you look up, and its towers overtop the city's tallest buildings. It looms beyond the ends of the streets like some gargantuan structure belonging more to the sky than to the earth, rising above the bay and the swarming shores like a sudden, blazing affirmation.

The Golden Gate Bridge, too, can only be grasped in terms of its full setting. Watch it from one of San Francisco's hills on a summer afternoon when the fog is flooding through the strait like a river, waves of vapor breaking over the deck, or when the entire span is enveloped and you see only vague glimpses of a mammoth tower or an arc of the deck or a web of cables as the curtains of moisture are momentarily parted.

Or see it when the air is clear, and the entire lithe red span is outlined against the dark cliffs and surf-fringed headlands of Marin. You know then that this structure has a meaning of its own. This is no urban bridge. It belongs not to the cities but to the continent's edge, to the wild coastline, the giant winds, the rising tides, the rolling ocean.

It is fitting that the bridge traverses this spectacular meeting of land and sea in a single mighty leap. For the building of the bridge was itself a leap—in engineering, in economics, in total imagination. Into this bridge flowed much of the genius of twentieth-century America—the scientific knowledge, the technical skill, the persistence in the face of setbacks, and above all the impulse to venture into the untried and unknown, to take the risk, to bridge the unbridgeable, to dare the impossible.

If the Bay Bridge represents the best of urban America today, the Golden Gate Bridge is a symbol of the future—of the opportunity that glimmers around the shores of this ocean for men who can grasp the meaning and promise of this age, a meaning written in steel in this soaring span at the Western Gate.

14

Tide of Empire

Go now to the narrows of the strait where the ocean has cleft
the western mountain wall and invaded the continent. Stand
near the old fort on the southern shore, where the colossus of
the Gate arches across the sky from headland to headland
above the racing tide.

The sun gleams from the white-capped waves of the ebbing
current, from the bright red steel of the bridge in the sky,
from the wind-ruffled blue waters of the inner bay, from the
white towers of the city rising like monoliths from the peninsular hills.

A black freighter, outbound for the Orient, moves through
the strait on the tide, partly disappears behind the massive
base of the bridge tower, then emerges, its bow beginning to
rise and fall in the ocean surge. Several long-necked cormorants skim the water nearby, batting their wings furiously

against the wind. A single white gull wheels in the air currents against a backdrop of the cities on the bay's eastern shore.

This tide flowing swiftly outward beneath the bridge carries the waters of the rivers from the high granite ridges and glacial fountains of the Sierra—waters of Shasta, Tuolumne, Yosemite, Kings, waters which have flowed through mine tailings of the Mother Lode, past the cities and orchards of the Sacramento, the cotton fields of the San Joaquin, the vineyards of Sonoma, the rich peat gardens of the delta, the factories and cities of the bay.

This is Chrysopolae, the Western Gate, and the bay within it has become, as Frémont and Dana predicted, the center of a western empire, the "emporium of a new world, the awakened Pacific . . ."

Now, in the second half of the twentieth century, the prophecies take on new meaning. The Chrysoceras of Byzantium was the ancient crossroads between Europe and Asia, and the Chrysopolae of San Francisco is ready for a similar role. Now there is an "awakened Pacific" greater than Dana ever dreamed—in all the lands at the ends of the sea lanes which lead out the Golden Gate.

There, the peoples of renascent nations are beginning to seek bread and freedom and machines and books, and all the rumblings and stirrings along the far shores are harbingers of an age in the making. This bay can be the "emporium of a new world" of unimagined potentiality. The gate which opened inward on El Dorado now opens outward on the Orient.

Here the waters of the western rivers meet cresting waves from the far Pacific. Here they mingle with ocean brine which may have once washed across the white coral atolls of the Marshalls, slapped against the wharves at Hong Kong, swirled in rip currents at Yokohama, thundered against the icy Siberian sea cliffs of Kamchatka, flowed in tidal rhythms along all the coasts of Asia. The long earth-circling migrations of Occidental man have brought him at last to this ultimate shore, facing across the final ocean the land of his beginnings.

Tomorrow lies west. It is being shaped at this moment beyond the setting sun. It is brewing in the conjunction of ocean rivers and moving masses of air far out on the face of the North Pacific. It is being conceived out of the impact of historical forces of titanic power and magnitude around the shores of this sea. Its visible symbol is this Gate at the edge of the continent. More than ever, in the Era of the Pacific, this will be the bay of destiny.

Index